Hāpai nā Leo

Hāpai nā Leo

Edited by Bill Teter

with Sage U'ilani Takehiro
Assistant Editor

15 14 13 12 11 10   1 2 3 4 5 6

ISBN 978-1-58351-088-9

Curriculum Research & Development Group Staff
Donald B. Young, Director
Kathleen F. Berg, Associate Director
Morris K. Lai, Pihana Nā Mamo Principal Investigator
Hugh H. Dunn, Pihana Nā Mamo Project Director
Lori Ward, Managing Editor
Leela M. Kumaran, Permissions
Jaret K. C. Leong, Production Coordinator

Cover design by Robin M. Clark
Cover art courtesy of Bishop Museum
Book design and layout by Robin M. Clark

Distributed by the
Curriculum Research & Development Group
College of Education
University of Hawaiʻi
1776 University Avenue
Honolulu, HI 96822-2463

crdg@hawaii.edu
www.hawaii.edu/crdg

This book is part of Pihana Nā Mamo: The Native Hawaiian Special
Education Project (Grant Number: H221A000002), funded by the U.S.
Department of Education under the Native Hawaiian Education Program
as authorized under Part B of Title VII of the Elementary and Secondary
Education Act of 1965 (ESEA), as amended by the No Child Left Behind Act
of 2001 (P.L. 107–110), and administered by the Office of Special Education
Programs, Office of Elementary and Secondary Education, U.S. Department
of Education. Opinions expressed herein are those of the authors and do not
necessarily reflect the position of the U.S. Department of Education, and such
endorsement should not be inferred.

In memory of Olga and Noah Kalama

CONTENTS

'Ohana

Kulāiwi

Pono

3 THE VOICES OF THE FUTURE

4 QUESTIONS FOR DISCUSSION AND WRITING

A NOTE ON HAWAIIAN WORDS AND THEIR SPELLING

The selections in *Hāpai nā Leo* come from a variety of sources and were written over a period of many years. As a result, there is little consistency in either the italicizing of Hawaiian words or the use of kahakō (macrons) and ʻokina (glottal stops). The editorial board of the journal *ʻŌiwi* explained in their second issue that they believed it best to leave the spelling of Hawaiian words as they were done by the authors. Following their lead, no spellings of Hawaiian words in any of the selections included in this anthology have been altered from the original text. Some authors use Hawaiian and Hawaiʻi Creole English interchangeably with English words and spellings, which are available for definition in most Hawaiian, English, or Pidgin English dictionaries. Readers are encouraged to reference dictionaries to support their interpretations of these works and to enhance their vocabulary in general.

Hoʻomākaukau . . .
>   the call begins
>   the grounds are ready
>   the ocean awaits

>   the anticipation builds
>   the moment nears

>   when we join forces and become one
>   human, nature and energy
>   become sport

Hoʻomākaukau . . .
>   the call begins
>   the grounds are ready
>   the ocean awaits

>   and Lono speaks

>   Pā.

>   – "Hoʻomākaukau,"
>   by Imaikalani Kalahele

One night Chris and I had been in our office for hours, talking story. It was late, almost 10 o'clock. As the room had darkened we hadn't bothered with the harsh overhead lights. Instead, Chris turned on our three computers, which gave our cramped office just enough light to read our students' writing to one another.

"You boys still here?" Noah asked, sticking his head in our office door. "How come you nevah turn on da lights?"

Noah's wife taught Hawaiian language at our school, and he was the school's unofficial (and unpaid) groundskeeper. Noah and Olga planted the noni and mango trees in the school courtyard, and the plumeria and kukui that bordered the parking lot. He worked the grounds just about every day.

Noah joined us that night. Chris read him a story written by his nephew, a junior at our school. Noah's eyes glistened with pride as he listened. "Bobby's a good boy," he said when Chris was finished. Chris responded, "He's a great writer."

We sat quietly in the semi-darkness while Noah's gentle voice filled the room. He began to talk stories of Olga's mother being taken away to Kalaupapa; his rascal days growing up in Papakōlea; the time he encountered his 'aumakua, a shark that head-butted him in the waters off Mānana island. As he talked, his face was moonlike, half in shadow, half lit by computer light. For a moment, it seemed to me his face dissolved into that of an ancestor, generations before, sitting beside a fire at night, and talking story. Only this ancestor's stories were lit by the illumination of today's technologies.

I've never forgotten that night: the music of Noah's voice; the gleam of his half lit face; the computer light serving as a modern-day version of a fire's glow. For centuries the rich body of Hawaiian literature was oral; maybe that's part of why people here speak of *talking* story rather than *telling* stories – because story is, in these islands, a way of talking.

When Mary Pukui, Samuel Elbert, and Esther Moʻokini published their *Place Names of Hawaii* in 1974, they placed the following quote at the front of the book as an epigraph:

> *Ua hala nā kūpuna, a he ʻike kōliʻuliʻu wale nō kō keia lā,*
> *i nā mea i ke au i hope lilo, iō kikilo.*

> The ancestors have passed on; today's people see but dimly
> times long gone and far behind.

In times of urban development, *Place Names of Hawaii* serves as historical documentation that preserves significant knowledge of Hawaiʻi's changing environments. This Hawaiian quote may be interpreted in many different ways within the conceptual context of ʻŌlelo Hawaiʻi. "Iō kikilo" may refer to the future as much as it refers to the past, as the two dimensions are connected through lineage.

Hāpai nā Leo is a literary companion to Malcolm Nāea Chun's historical and philosophical works, the Ka Wana series, published by the Curriculum Research & Development Group, and *No Nā Mamo*, published by the University of Hawaiʻi Press. This anthology responds with collected perspectives far-ranging in style, form, and generations. They address broad, yet specific, topics: sovereignty and power; economics and social relationships; identity and spirituality. While these perspectives represent particular stories and places, they remind us that all people struggle to define themselves in ways large and small, public and private, individual and communal.

Book-ended by representations of our past and our future, the Voices of Hawaiʻi are grouped into four themes: Kekahi, ʻOhana, Kulāiwi, and Pono. Many of the readings overlap from one category into another; few focus specifically on one central idea or Hawaiian value. These section headings contextualize an interpretation of the readings and provide a focal point for students and other readers to probe their own thoughts through discussion, writing, or talking story. The themes suggest a general movement of aware-ness from the individual to the collective. This movement is a growing real-ization of individual ties that connect us to the world and the people around us—much like the way each knot in a fisherman's net carries sustenance to nourish a community.

Kekahi presents several voices exploring different searches to understand the role of ancestry as it applies to individual identity. Kahi Brooks painfully wonders if her ancestors would even know her today:

> Would they see me
> pale, blue jeans, Frappucino
> and find me more foreign than haole
> My Ford more strange than the *Endeavor*,
> or would they see me
> (Tūtū can you see me?!)
> and know me as their own

The answer she receives is wonderfully healing. In "Culture Blind," the young author Holo Hoʻopai gives us a portrait of a boy struggling to understand what the values and traditions of the past could mean to him, while John Hoʻomanawanui speaks of "Moving forward by looking back." This section shows identity conflicts and resolution through exploring the self in relation to familial or cultural contexts, which sets a foundation for the second section, ʻOhana.

The authors in ʻOhana provide broad interpretations of ʻohana. We meet a number of families and family members here. Some stories in this section exemplify how ʻohana refers to more than just our biological families. The concept of ʻohana can extend to a network of people sharing their lives together. Jasmine Tua's "They Called Him Mango Man" goes beyond traditional concepts of family and household structures through her narrator's observations. The connections we have with others reflect our identities, as these relationships help shape our individual form. These collective individualities are symbolized in Imaikalani Kalahele's poem "Make Rope," which refers to connections among people, places, and things. This section of *Hāpai nā Leo* speaks to notions of connectivity, tying ʻOhana to Kulāiwi.

Kulāiwi specifies Hawaiian cultural perspectives about certain sources of individual and collective existence. Keith Kalani Akana's "Press Down" commands a connection to the earth with symbols of a tree from root to blossom. George Kahumoku, Jr. takes us out into the ocean to encounter a shark, while Makia Malo exemplifies a human relationship to taro in more than just symbolic ways. Marjorie Sinclair lets us feel the hot breath of Pele while she shares with us the endless circle of destruction and renewal in "Lava Watch." Haunani-Kay Trask celebrates the characteristics of regeneration in her poem "To Hear the Mornings." Bryan Wake plays on the nature of the ocean, referring to it as a living being. This section exemplifies relationships and experiences with those non-human elements that people are connected to. Individual and collective identities are balanced with those peoples and environments they come from, as well as an awareness of where they are going.

The collection of readings in Pono balances the concepts of Kekahi, 'Ohana, and Kulāiwi, weaving them into a whole. Mary Beth Aldosa raises the potentially uncomfortable, yet necessarily rich and healing question of who is Hawaiian in her story, "'Au 'A 'Ia." Puanani Burgess and Manu Aluli Meyer offer essays on personal identity and the role of education in its development. Matthew Kaopio provokes thoughts about the concepts of home. Lee Cataluna's *Super Secret Squad* addresses many pressing issues, using humor as an effective literary device to describe some dynamics of activism and interpretation. In the end, the last word belongs to 'Anakala Kalāhele, lecturing us in Sage U'ilani Takehiro's prose poem: "So mo' bettah Love den Hate brah, mo bettah love den hate—you know why? Cuz can."

Cuz can. Perfect.

Language is an important factor in expressing the kind of balance today's people seek to achieve. This anthology is articulated in formal English as well as Hawai'i Creole English and 'Ōlelo Hawai'i. Each language carries meanings that can only survive if kept within the context of its original, untranslatable diction. However, these meanings have diverse connotations based on the contextual environments in which our interpretations take place and the situations that we apply them to. The reality of multiple languages functioning together liberates multiple meanings, multiple thoughts, and multiple interpretations.

The final voices in our collection are two poets from Youth Speaks Hawai'i. "Kaona," written by Jamaica Osorio and Ittai Wong, rings with pride and urgency. It celebrates the power of language, confronts the injustices of the past (and present), and calls on all of us to—well, to *speak*. These young performance poets slammed "Kaona" at the June 2008 Brave New Voices International Youth Poetry Festival at the Smithsonian Institution in Washington, DC, where the Hawai'i Youth Speaks Team won first place in the competition. The delivery of "Kaona" includes an oli chanted by teammates Alaka'i Kotrys and Will Giles who took a stand in the audience and responded to their teammates on stage with "E Hō Mai" written by Aunty Edith Kanaka'ole.

The legacy of Hawaiian literature is carried into the future by works such as "Kaona," with voices that bust through dominant structures of language, weaving poetry and prayer from the past and the present. "Kaona" exemplifies the educational representation of 'ohana and kulāiwi through the balance of language, empowering these young voices as individuals.

As Osorio and Wong conclude,

Without language, we have nothing
We must see to it that our language survives like the past, through flowers
Ua ola ka olelo mai ka paiku ana o na pua
E hiki na pua e ola mai ka paiku ana o ka olelo
So our children can survive, through the passing of language

As long as there are voices like theirs and the others in this book, there will be legacies for the future of Hawai'i, and perseverance toward a balance of our individuality, our families, and our homeland.

We accept the challenge, the invitation to learn, to confront injustice, to restore balance and move forward, to raise our voices in celebration of that movement, to make central to our lives everything implied by the vital breath of aloha.

The Voices of Beginnings

KUMULIPO

excerpt from

AN ACCOUNT OF THE CREATION OF THE WORLD

ACCORDING TO HAWAIIAN TRADITION
TRANSLATED FROM ORIGINAL MANUSCRIPTS PRESERVED EXCLUSIVELY IN HER
MAJESTY'S FAMILY

by Liliuokalani of Hawaii

THE FIRST ERA, OR AGE.

FIRST VERSE

At the time that turned the heat of the earth,
At the time when the heavens turned and changed,
At the time when the light of the sun was subdued
To cause light to break forth,
At the time of the night of Makalii (winter)
Then began the slime which established the earth,
The source of deepest darkness.
Of the depth of darkness, of the depth of darkness,
Of the darkness of the sun, in the depth of night,
        It is night,
        So was night born.

SECOND VERSE

Kumulipo was born in the night, a male.
Poele was born in the night, a female.
A coral insect was born, from which was born perforated coral.
The earth worm was born, which gathered earth into mounds,
From it were born worms full of holes.
The starfish was born, whose children were born starry.
The phosphorous was born, whose children were born phosphorescent.
The Ina was born Ina (sea egg).

The Halula was born Halula (sea urchin).
The Hawae was born, the Wana-ku was its offspring.
The Haukeuke was born, the Uhalula was its offspring.
The Pioe was born, the Pipi was its offspring (clam oyster).
The Papaua was born, the Olepe was its offspring (pearl and oyster).
The Nahawele was born, the Unauna was its offspring
                    (muscle and crab in a shell).

The Makaiaulu was born, the Opihi was its offspring.
The Leho was born, the Puleholeho was its offspring (cowry).
The Naka was born, its offspring was Kupekala (rock oysters).
The Makaloa was born, the Pupuawa was its offspring.
The Ole was born, the Oleole was its offspring (conch).
The Pipipi was born, the Kupee was its offspring (limpets).

Kane was born to Waiololi, a female to Waiolola.
The Wi was born, the Kiki was its offspring.
The Akaha's home was the sea;
Guarded by the Ekahakaha that grew in the forest.
A night of flight by noises
Through a channel; water is life to trees;
So the gods may enter, but not man.

THIRD VERSE
Man by Waiololi, woman by Waiolola,
The Akiaki was born and lived in the sea;
Guarded by the Manienie Akiaki that grew in the forest.
A night of flight by noises
Through a channel; water is life to trees;
So the gods may enter, but not man.

FOURTH VERSE
Man by Waiololi, woman by Waiolola,
The Aalaula was born and lived in the sea;
Guarded by the Alaalawainui that grew in the forest.
A night of flight by noises
Through a channel; water is life to trees;
So the gods may enter, but not man.

FIFTH VERSE
Man by Waiololi, woman by Waiolola,
The Manauea was born and lived in the sea;
Guarded by the Kalo Manauea that grew in the forest.
A night of flight by noises
Through a channel; water is life to trees;
So the gods may enter, but not man.

SIXTH VERSE
Man by Waiololi, woman by Waiolola,
The Koeleele was born and lived in the sea;
Guarded by the Ko punapuna Koeleele that grew in the forest.
A night of flight by noises
Through a channel; water is life to trees;
So the gods may enter, but not man.

SEVENTH VERSE
Man by Waiololi, woman by Waiolola,
The Puaiki was born and lived in the sea;
Guarded by the Lauaki that grew in the forest.
A night of flight by noises
Through a channel; water is life to trees;
So the gods may enter, but not man.

EIGHTH VERSE
Man by Waiololi, woman by Waiolola,
The Kikalamoa was born and lived in the sea;
Guarded by the Moamoa that grew in the forest.
A night of flight by noises
Through a channel; water is life to trees;
So the gods may enter, but not man.

NINTH VERSE
Man by Waiololi, woman by Waiolola,
The Limukele was born and lived in the sea;
Guarded by the Ekele that grew in the forest.
A night of flight by noises
Through a channel; water is life to trees;
So the gods may enter, but not man.

TENTH VERSE
Man by Waiololi, woman by Waiolola,
The Limukala was born and lived in the sea;
Guarded by the Akala that grew in the forest.
A night of flight by noises
Through a channel; water is life to trees;
So the gods may enter, but not man.

ELEVENTH VERSE

Man by Waiololi, woman by Waiolola,

The Lipuupuu was born and lived in the sea;

Guarded by the Lipuu that grew in the forest.

A night of flight by noises

Through a channel; water is life to trees;

So the gods may enter, but not man.

TWELFTH VERSE

Man by Waiololi, woman by Waiolola,

The Loloa was born and lived in the sea;

Guarded by the Kalamaloloa that grew in the forest.

A night of flight by noises

Through the channel; water is life to trees;

So the gods may enter, but not man.

THIRTEENTH VERSE

Man by Waiololi, woman by Waiolola,

The Ne was born and lived in the sea;

Guarded by the Neneleau that lived in the forest.

A night of flight by noises

Through the channel; water is life to trees;

So the gods may enter, but not man.

FOURTEENTH VERSE

Man by Waiololi, woman by Waiolola,

The Hulu-waena was born and lived in the sea;

Guarded by the Huluhulu Ieie that grew in the forest.

A night of flight by noises

Through the channel; water is life to trees;

So the gods may enter, but not man.

FIFTEENTH VERSE

A husband of gourd, and yet a god,
A tendril strengthened by water and grew
A being, produced by earth and spread,
Made deafening by the swiftness of Time
Of the Hee that lengthened through the night,
That filled and kept on filling
Of filling, until, filled
To filling, 'tis full,
And supported the earth, which held the heaven
On the wing of Time, the night is for Kumulipo (creation),
                    'Tis night.

The Voices of Hawai‘i

KEKAHI

MOEʻUHANE

Joseph P. Balaz

I dream of
the ways of the past —

I cannot go back.

I hike the hills
   and valleys of Wahiawā,
walking through crystal
         streams
  and scaling green cliffs.

I play in the waves
       of Waimea,
  and spear fish
   from the reefs of Kawailoa.

I grow bananas, ʻulu,
      and papayas,
   in the way of the ʻāina.

I cannot go back —

I never left.

ISLAND BORN

Keola Beamer

Driving my car in the evening air, cruising down the road
I hear a voice on the radio, singing music sweet and low

Winding through the valley, to the windward side
Seems like everything I see, is somehow a part of me, and I am proud to be,
Island Born.

I don't know where I'm going, and I got no place to be
Feeling grateful in my soul, to call this land my home, and so proud to be
Island Born.

Island Born. From the Mountain, to the sea, so proud to be, Island Born
Island Born
From the Mountain, to the sea, so proud to be, Island Born

Sunrise on the mountain, moving o'er the trees
And I will lift my eyes to see, this day you've given me, so proud to be to be,
Island Born.

Island Born.
From the Mountain, to the sea, so proud to be, Island Born,
Island Born
From the Mountain, to the sea, so proud to be, Island Born

Island Born

THE SHIMMERING – KA ‘OLILI

Keola Beamer

I breathe raggedly, my sides heaving from the exertion of running through the dense underbrush. I have run so far and so hard that I can taste the metallic flavor of my own blood. It wells up in my lungs and foams at the edge of my mouth. Behind me, the ravenous wailing shifts upward in pitch. Soon they will be upon me.

Ahead there is a change in the scent-pattern of the forest. The fragrance of the ‘ōhi‘a bark is undercut by the dark and musky smell of damp earth. It is my beloved. She offers her own body to shield me from the pursuing beasts. As tendrils of thick gray fog reach down through the high branches of the ‘ōhi‘a lehua trees, I chant her name. I sniff the air and move cautiously towards the hidden entrance of the cave.

The fog parts for my passage and swirls down the embankment, moving among the dark red blossoms of lehua. In the upland forest, the first stars appear through the high canopy of leaves. Seeing the points of light, I am lost in the reverie of my thoughts. Perhaps when one is close to death, memories of life unfold to ease the passage. I recall the curve of her neck, and the way I pressed her to the earth, her hair flowing around her body like a soft, black wave. I breathe more evenly and I smile. She has taught me to appreciate the mysterious beauty of the forest and even in the destruction I have caused, the beauty persists. A cold wind descends from the mountain, and as the mist swirls amongst the uprooted hāpu‘u, their grotesque and fallen stumps sail gently beneath the soft glow of a crescent moon.

The howling pack of canines approach, tearing through the shrubbery. I can almost feel the gnashing of their serrated and deadly teeth. The hair on my back bristles. I have only moments left. I flee to the cave and penetrate her warm darkness. Praying that the wind will blow my scent further into the depths and away from the pursuing beasts, I kneel beneath the dripping ceiling.

There will be another time, another life. I have reached the end of my journey. Holding her name just once more on my tongue, I settle in the darkness and begin ka ‘olili – the shimmering.

When the hunters come crashing through the undergrowth, their weapons become entangled in the ‘ama‘uma‘u and the ‘uhaloa. It is as I wish, but in the swirling mist, the lead dog of the pack breaks free of the stubborn weeds and runs snarling into the dark entrance of the cave. He is a devil dog, that one, and somehow he has found me. When his jaws open and he lunges for the soft flesh of my side, I chant to my beloved —

Kekē ho'i ka niho	The teeth are exposed
'Ane'ane nanahu mai	Ready to bite
Moku au lā	I am bitten,
Moku au lā.	I am bitten.

I scream in agony.

Her voice, like no other, responds in haste. I hear the deep rumbling beneath the earth, the swift tremor of her anger moving down the flanks of *Kīlauea*, towards the sea. In the closeness of the cave, the devil dog is frightened. He loosens his jaws and backs away.

* * * * * * * * * *

"Eh Manny, you not going believe dis," the hunter says, shining the big flashlight in my face. My hair is entangled with dry twigs and *honohono* grass. Saliva hangs from the side of my mouth.

"Why one big *haole* hippie wen come insai hea?" the other one says, sheathing the knife. He kneels beside me and raises my head. "Mus' be mushroom or something. Da guy naked, he stay stone out of his mind." The beam from the flashlight moves down my body. "Eh . . . shit, da buggah bleeding." The light illuminates the pool of blood next to my side. The other hunter reaches for his pack. There are two beams of light now, both men aiming their flashlights at the glistening pool of my blood. The beams of light move erratically, reflections glowing on the far wall of the cave. The reflected light paints the cave red.

"Call the KMC ambulance fo' come quick, Derek."

"Stupid mutt," Derek says, dragging the animal out by the loose folds of skin on his neck. He gives it a hard kick with his boot. The big dog growls and scurries away. The hunter straightens up from the entrance of the dripping cave and lifts the walkie-talkie to his mouth.

Strapped to the gurney, I roll slowly towards the ambulance. The wheels lurch in the loose gravel and the bright red emergency light flashes repeatedly on my face. Through the drizzling rain, I can see a fine mist hovering in the moonlight. The shining red beacon reflects from the wet boughs and the tangle of *'ōhi'a* trees surrounding the parking lot. Engines 12 and 17 idle on the wet asphalt, their exhausts misting in the cool air. The men are tired and cold, their muscles aching from the long haul down the trail. They stand beside the fire trucks, smoking cigarettes, putting away ropes and emergency gear. I blink as the *ua li'ili'i*, the light rain, clings to my beard and the lashes of my eyes. The emergency medics slide the gurney into the back of the ambulance and close the door. I do not resist. I lie exhausted beneath the sheets. When we are bloodied, it takes longer for the *'olili* to complete.

The ambulance moves across the parking lot in the light rain. The vehicle picks up speed and crosses the centerline of the wet pavement. I hear the tires drumming on the lane dividers of Volcano Highway. In the confines of the ambulance, the scent of the Emergency Medical Technician next to me reaches my nostrils. A sour aroma emanates from the perspiration in the hollow beneath his left arm. I suspect that he has an undiagnosed form of lymphatic cancer. He will be dead soon. The uniformed medic works quickly to attach the intravenous line into the thick vein of my left arm. When the solution drips slowly, he seems satisfied.

He asks slowly and clearly, "Who are you?" He looks closely at my face. "What is your name?"

I raise my head and struggle to respond: "***Ka haole nui maka 'ālohilohi,***" I growl softly. I cannot speak. After the *'olili* there is a period of alignment, a period of silence and fog. It is in this space that the shadow of the *kino lau* is released. I will wait to speak again.

The medic puts his gloved hand on my forehead and says, "Easy now. It's O.K., take it easy."

I lay my head back down on the gurney and close my eyes. I am *ka haole nui maka 'ālohilohi*, I am the large foreigner with the bright eyes. It is my blood that seeps through the white gauze. As the ambulance speeds down the incline, I listen to the rain and the swoosh of tires on the wet pavement. I begin to remember who I am. The content of my thoughts, at first expressed in the Hawaiian language, metamorphoses into English as the *'olili* finally solidifies.

My name is Kenneth Weir. I was born in the winter of 1964 in Socorro, New Mexico. I am unmarried. I have no siblings. My parents were killed in an automobile accident when I was 17 years old. I am six feet two inches tall. I have brown hair and I weigh 217 pounds. I am a volcanologist; I undertake the classification of volcanic activity and study the nature and causes of volcanic eruptions.

I served a brief internship at Stromboli, an active volcano that lies on an island off the coast of Italy. I came to the Hawaii Volcanoes National Park

Observatory in 1994 as a research associate. I am currently employed in seismic data correlation for the National Park Service.

I was working at the observatory and writing my dissertation in volcanology when Nicholas Granger, one of the Park's senior scientists, invited me to his home for dinner. Nicholas had a fondness for me and took me under his guidance at the Observatory. Over a glass of merlot, he intimated that it might be a good idea for me to "broaden the base of my understanding." I wasn't quite following him at first. Nicholas was something of a radical in our field in that he believed that a life based solely on intellectual acquisition was incomplete. He was a proponent of contextual learning. As Nicholas described it, this was learning that occurs in close relationship with actual experience. Since the study of Hawaiian volcanology could not conceivably be separated from the word "Hawaiian," Nicholas was suggesting that I might be missing part of the equation. I was listening intently when he suggested it might be good for me to learn the Hawaiian language, implying that what I learned would aid in the development of the historical references outlined in my dissertation. When he discovered that I was generally receptive to this idea, he further recommended that I join one of the *hālau hula* on the Island. He saw this as a way to gain a more balanced perspective of my work "from within a cultural context." Since I respected Nicholas a great deal, I gave these ideas considerable deliberation. Both suggestions intrigued me. The University of Hawaii at Hilo was widely recognized as having the best Hawaiian language department in the state and I had heard that there were several *hālau* of merit located nearby.

After a period of investigation and earnest inquiry, I was invited to join a *hālau hula* in Hilo town. In a few short months, I was studying the basics of the art form called *hula*. At approximately the same time, I enrolled at the University and began my studies of *'ōlelo Hawai'i* – the Hawaiian language. My studies and work at the observatory continued without interruption. I experienced a true love for the things I was learning. I began to understand that all around us, the unique aspect of things Hawaiian were diminishing in the hurried pace of the 21st century. These sad contemplations came to me at night when I was alone in my cabin.

At the end of the next year, the men in the *hālau* moved towards the study of *kahiko*. *Kahiko* was the ancient form of Hawaiian dance and we met to chant and dance for several days of each week. I was a good student; I worked hard, I listened to the *kumu hula*, and I learned the rudiments of fixed movement in time that comprise the basic elements of *kahiko*. It took a while for my big *haole* body to understand and feel the rhythm. At first, I was *hemahema*, awkward and unskilled, but I kept at it. Perhaps someday, I hoped, I could become a decent practitioner of the art of *hula kahiko*.

I matriculated into third year Hawaiian language as the *hālau* focused on a series of chants honoring the Fire Goddess Pele. As soon as this endeavor commenced, I experienced an integral sense of peace, a quiet grounding of my spirit. I felt at my best with these chants. My complete acceptance of them and, it seems, of them to me, was a mysterious epiphany. In a manner of speaking, I experienced a religious conversion. A feeling of warmth and completeness washed over me each time *Kumu* raised his voice to chant –

> *Aia lā ʻo Pele i Hawaiʻi ʻeā, ke haʻa maila i Maukele ʻeā*
> *ʻŪhī, ʻūhā mai ana ʻeā, ke nome aʻela i nā Puna ʻeā*
> *Ka mea nani ka i Paliuli ʻeā, ke pulelo aʻela i nā pali ʻeā*

As the months went by, I made slow progress in the completion of my dissertation. I continued my study of the Pele chants and I continued dancing with the *hālau*. Except for the occasional bout of loneliness, I felt that I had a good life. I enjoyed the rich cultural tapestry of the Hawaiian people and on a professional level, my work at the Observatory was interesting and intellectually rewarding. In short, I was content.

But this contentment was an illusion.

One afternoon, I was sitting at my desk at the Observatory, adjusting the calibration of a tiltometer, when suddenly a Hawaiian hawk, an *ʻio*, landed on the ledge of the window and raked its sharp claws across the thick pane of glass. The noise of those brittle claws against the glass startled me. I snapped my head up and looked at the window. It was eerie. The dark bird stared in at me intensely as the seismograph in the corner plotted a long upward arc. On the monitor of my computer screen, a message coalesced from the vaporous, green phosphors. It said:

Come, my beloved

The skin on my arm turned to gooseflesh. The *ʻio* shrieked and flew from the window ledge. A few seconds later, the message was gone and the screen returned to the data I was running. How odd, I thought, rubbing my tingling arm and logging into the system administrator files. I was checking to see who had tapped into my computer. Willard Drakes, the new supervisor, was a difficult, irritating man. Maybe he had suddenly developed a sense of humor. More likely, this was a hacker trying to break in to our network from outside. I ran a complete access check and found no other users logged on to the system. I walked around the lab, peeking into the partially opened door of the administration office. Drakes wasn't even in the building. I ran a complete virus scan, checked the firewall and again found nothing. This is extremely odd, I thought. Extremely odd. I backed up the data, executed a low level re-formatting of the main drive and went to lunch.

In the small dining room that day, the lasagna seemed unappetizing. The fresh avocados that someone had brought from home and placed on the counter seemed much more appealing. The texture of the avocados felt good in my mouth and the flavor was exquisite. I felt guilty, eating several of them, piling the green skins high on my plastic tray.

That night, I lay in my bed reading Martha Beckwith's "Hawaiian Mythology." I drifted off. Instead of sleeping soundly, as I usually did, I experienced a disturbing dream. In the vivid mental imagery, I scurried through the caliginous growth of the forest floor. I was moving swiftly, down low to the ground, as the forest around me exploded in fascinating colors and smells.

At the observatory the next day, we had a small celebration in honor of Nicholas, who was leaving for a year's sabbatical. Some of the staff had bought cake and ice cream. I had constructed a *lei haku*, made of *laua'e* fern and *liko lehua*. I placed the *lei* on his shoulders, shook his hand heartily and wished him luck. I was sad that Nicholas was leaving. I had wanted more time with him to discuss my mystifying computer problems. After the festivities, Supervisor Drakes approached my desk with his hands in his pockets and a tight smile. He said, "Weir, clean up this crap before you leave. This is a professional institution, not a high school prom." He was referring to the small leaves and bits of *liko* that had fallen on the floor from the *lei haku*. It was Drake's way of warning me that now that Nicholas was gone, I had better watch my step.

During my studies with the *hālau*, I met an attractive woman named Cassandra. She was a divorcee, in her third year at UH Hilo. Sometimes I'd pick her up and take her to see a movie in town. We seemed to enjoy each other's company. I was hoping that our relationship would lead to something more substantial, but I wasn't quite sure if she felt the same way. Cassandra and her roommate had three large dogs. Often, when I went to pick her up, I brought a pull-toy or a rubber ball. I'd play with the dogs in the driveway while I waited for her to get ready. As I played with them that day, I detected a strange metallic scent emanating from inside the house. It was the smell of blood and something else. Cassandra came to the porch and said that she was not feeling well. She said she would prefer to stay home and rest.

"Are you feeling all right?" I asked.

"Just female trouble," she mentioned, somewhat embarrassed, "I'm having my period."

We have an alternating schedule at the Observatory. I was working the night shift again, correlating seismic data. The wind picked up suddenly from the crater, howling along the ridgeline and under the eves of the building. It was two o'clock in the morning when another terrifying missive appeared on my screen. This time, the green phosphors telegraphed:

I chant from deep within - your name so sweet
Kama - my own

The lateness of the hour and the fact that I was alone in the building increased my apprehension. The message really scared me. I ran all the computer checks I could think of and came up, again, with nothing. I was not a computer novice. I had worked around the damn things my entire professional life, but something very strange was happening here and it was infuriating. I emailed Drakes and requested that a qualified technician examine the operating system of every single computer in the system. Feeling tired and wired at the same time, I logged out from my machine and left the premises.

The sky was pink that early morning and the caustic smell of vog lingered along the highway. I opened the window of the jeep and felt the cold air engulf me. I inhaled the fumes deeply, smiling at the acrid smell. I was glad to be away from New Mexico and the dry expanse of red desert soil. I liked it here in the mist and the rain; I felt good in these Islands. I had my work. I had the *hālau*. I had my dissertation. Lost in these thoughts, I barely noticed the dark wings of a *pueo*, trailing effortlessly in the rear view mirror.

I drove to my small cabin in *Kīlauea*. My needs there were simple. A small wood-burning fireplace, a kitchen table, a few chairs, a desk, a bed. I took off my muddy boots and walked into the kitchen to make myself breakfast. I began by arranging the ingredients on the counter: mushrooms, onion, cheese. I pulled a dozen eggs out of the refrigerator and opened the cover of the container. The raw eggs looked so beautiful. I studied each one of them, lined up and nestled in the gray cardboard box. I felt my pulse quicken as I took a single egg from the carton, cupped it in my hand and brought it up to my nostrils, sniffing inquisitively. I placed the egg at eye level and studied its shape closely, admiring the porous, white surface of the shell. I rolled it gently in my fingers, feeling its weight. So round and smooth. So perfect. I extended my tongue and licked it softly. I licked it again, moving my tongue along the cool circumference. The egg had a clean taste, suggesting a deliciousness within. I placed the whole egg in between my teeth. I bit down slowly, cracking the shell and spilling the yolk and whites into my warm mouth. I cradled the yolk in my tongue, rolling it from side to side. Unable to contain my hunger any longer, I bit down abruptly. When the yolk burst and ran between my teeth, I swallowed greedily. It was an incredibly luscious taste. The flavor of the raw egg caused me to salivate uncontrollably. Bending over the small stainless steel sink, I consumed eight more eggs, gulping them down, shell and all. My thick saliva, the yolks and the whites, dripped from both sides of my mouth, splattering down the front of my flannel shirt.

At the observatory, Drakes came angrily up to my desk and threw the tech requisition on my desk.

"What the hell is this, Weir? We are not examining every damn computer in the building. Are you out of your mind?"

"Drakes," I tried to explain, "there's a real possibility of data corruption, if we can't . . ."

Drakes wouldn't let me finish, he put his hands on his hips and bellowed, "Then why don't you and your *lei* making friends wave some *ti* leaves around and voodoo the damn things. We are NOT spending any money on this ridiculous request. Jesus H. Christ, Weir, get a goddamn grip!" He stomped away, fuming.

I called Cassandra. She was feeling better, so I went over to pick her up. I honked the horn and opened the door of the jeep, taking the rubber ball from my jacket pocket. The canines refused to engage in any activity with me at all, no matter how many times I entreated them. They waited apprehensively on the porch and sniffed cautiously as I came near. When I went up the stairs, one of the big Alsatians began whining and crawling on his belly. He lowered his head, flattened his ears back and urinated like a puppy.

A few days later, I was studying the printouts of seismic activity along the northern rift zone. A *nēnē* goose, disrupted by the flow of hot air upwards from the crater, crashed heavily into the main observatory window. The big bird screamed, leaving a trail of blood smeared across the thick glass. I felt a sense of deja vu and deep dread. I turned my head slowly to the right and looked at the seismograph readings. The reading that was coming in was very specific. The chart was displaying precise movements in time, as though there was a form of intelligence at work. My hands trembled as I held the printout. I looked at the baseline and the peaks and translated the reading into a rhythm felt somewhere in the center of my chest. The seismograph had

produced the definitive *kahiko* beat of the *pahu* drum; U U – U TE TE / U
U – U TE TE

Another message appeared, at my computer monitor, this time in *'ōlelo
Hawai'i*:

O Kama hoi paha oe,
Kanaka o ka pali ku
O ka pali moe
O ka pali kuhoho
O ka pali ka'a o ka pohaku.

I understood these words.

Thou art indeed Kama,
The man of the high cliffs,
Of the low lying cliffs,
Of the steep cliffs,
Of the cliffs of the rolling stones.

I stared at the monitor with an ashen face. Then I pulled the jacket close
to my body and shivered uncontrollably. My limbs were very cold. I read it
again. My flesh began to crawl. I wondered if I was losing my mind.

At *hālau* that week, our *kumu* demonstrated a form of low crouching
style called *'ai ha'a*. He said that it was very difficult and required considerable muscular strength in the upper thighs and calves. Though he was a
master dancer, he appeared to strain a bit in demonstrating the low squatting
movements of this style. In simple choreography accompanied by the large
pahu drum, we each took turns, knees bent, squatting, moving. I was the
last to attempt this exercise. To my surprise, the movement came easily. The
strength in my lower body seemed formidable. Somehow, without my even
noticing, the muscles in my stomach, thighs and calves had strengthened. It
seemed natural to me, to move along the ground, down close to the earth. As
the *pahu* beats continued, I expanded the movements of my body in concen-
tric circles radiating outward and moved lower . . . and lower, closer to the
wooden floor of the old gymnasium. I was moving very fast and very low,
the *pahu* thundering. As I danced, I began to lose myself and I felt as though
I was parting a veil, reentering the enigmatic forest world of the dream. As I
closed my eyes and began to move *'ai ha'a* through the low undergrowth, the
pahu drumming suddenly stopped.

I slowed my movement and closed. I straightened out uncomfortably and stood, turning to face the assembled students. The entire class was staring at me, their faces completely drained of color. I was sweating and breathing heavily in short, staccato *uh- uh –uh* noises. At first, no other sound could be heard. Then, in the damp silence, I heard the shuffling of their bare feet. Almost as one, they backed away from me. I looked cautiously around the big gymnasium as the smell of fear permeated the air.

On the way back up the hill, the rain came down heavily on Volcano Highway, splashing in big, fat drops on the windshield of the jeep. I pulled over at Hirano Store to buy something for dinner. When I saw the salad bags of *hō'i'o* fern tips, I paused, feeling intense hunger pangs. I held the bag, sniffing, and moving my nostrils up and down the outside of it. I paid for the bag at the small counter, but before I even got back to the car, I tore through the plastic with my teeth, snorting with joy as I reached the small, delicious shoots within. I stood outside the store, near a cluster of swaying, green bamboo and ate greedily.

I ran back inside the store and bought five more bags. I would consume each one of those bags as I sat, hunched over in the front seat of the jeep. An elderly Japanese woman in a Camry pulled in to the space next to me. When the small terrier in the back seat saw me, he howled maniacally, lunging with his small, bared teeth at the inside of the window. I wiped my mouth with the back of my hand, still relishing the taste of the fern shoots. The woman seemed unable to control the animal, her bewildered and frightened face blurred by the heavy drip of rain on the glass. I reversed the jeep quickly. The clamoring of the little dog faded as lightning zigzagged across the black sky.

That night, there was a terrible thunderstorm. The power to the Observatory stalled, then re-energized, the battery back-ups kicking in and out. From the Volcano House, all the way down to the coast, the storm unleashed its fury. It pummeled the trees, tremendous bolts of lightning tearing through the *'ōhi'a* leaves. In the crater, the mist swirled and swirled, spinning counter-clockwise in the ghostly cauldron of Halema'uma'u. As the worst of the storm stalled overhead, the security system of the building short-circuited, sending sparks flying across the room. The alarm system wailed and screamed in the building. One of the tiltometers on the southern flank illustrated a grotesque bulge in the earth. My stomach turned. This is impossible, I thought, struggling with my own sanity. In the horrible cacophony of the wind, rain and screaming alarms, my monitor flickered insanely and the streaking cursor messaged:

My beloved kane - more beautiful with each passing day

Trembling, almost useless, my fingers stabbed forcefully at the keyboard:

Who areYoU

Suddenly, the electrical power died in the lab and the computers crashed, their back-up circuits beeping intolerably. The shrieking alarms continued to wail until I could stand it no longer. I grabbed an emergency flashlight and left as quickly as I could, running through the puddles of the flooded parking lot. As I opened the door of the jeep, I could see lightning bursting in great sheets above the caldera. The world had gone insane. I was witnessing Nature, seized by dementia and wondering if perhaps, I too, was so afflicted. I shifted the jeep into gear and stomped on the accelerator.

I sped along the highway then pulled into the driveway of my small cabin. The branches of the *'ōhi'a lehua* were rubbing together, screeching and making sounds I had never heard. The trees swayed and shuddered in the onslaught of the howling wind. When I stepped out of the jeep, my boots sunk into the thick mud and I stood there in the pouring rain feeling lost and afraid. I took off my boots and my socks and I felt my bare feet sink into the cool, thick *lepo* of the driveway. The mud felt so good, so soothing. I walked slowly towards the steps of the porch, feeling the delicious wet earth beneath the arches of my feet. I looked towards the house. What I felt was inexplicable. The old house just didn't seem to suit me anymore. I thought of the small, uncomfortable chair at the kitchen table and the stiff bed in the back room. The house seemed unwelcoming, its furnishings awkward and unpleasant. Instead of going up the steps to the front door, I turned and walked to the small gate securing the crawl space beneath the house. I bent over and pushed it with my hand. The gate opened on screeching hinges.

I inhaled deeply. A musty, damp smell came from under the house. Hanging from the floor joists were long, ghostly wisps of spider webs, swinging in the blustering wind. I stared into the space, my eyes adjusting to the deep blackness. I found the low space comforting. I would be safe here, I knew. I removed my clothing, feeling the drops of rain on my bare chest. Then, I lowered myself *'ai ha'a* style into the sweet darkness. As I entered, the suspended cobwebs caught on my brow. Shredded bits of *liko lehua* and pieces of *'a'ali'i* drifted in with the storm to tangle in my hair. I raised my arms slowly and placed them in front of me, clasping both hands.

I pronounced the *kāhea*, *"Aia lā ʻo Pele i Hawaiʻi ʻeā,"* and paused. I didn't hold for long. The clouds cleared and the moon rose up magnificently from behind the ridge. Fingers of bluish-white moonlight reached for me through the latticework skirting the house. Above me, the striking thunder of the heavens synchronized into a distinct rhythmic pattern. **U U - U TE TE / U U - U TE TE** . It was the same fixed pattern of the seismograph reading. Inconceivably, the thunderclaps expressed the *pahu* beats of ancient *kahiko*.

I leapt into movement, dancing vigorously beneath the joists of the old floor. I circled in the damp earth, turning forward, turning back, the muscles in my thighs flexing and extending. I had never experienced this level of control over my own body before. It was as if my limbs were obeying my thoughts, not approximately, but exactly and precisely as I commanded. In raiment of spider-silk and the small shreds of leaves, I danced savagely in *ʻai haʻa* style. Though my body seemed capable of an incredible range of expression, the actual choreography or movement positions were telegraphed to me by a consciousness outside of my own. It was *hula* that was coming, not from me, but through me. The rhythmic cadences I enjoined were so powerful, so compelling that I felt inwardly changed. I was no longer afraid. I was no longer alone. I danced for those who had come before me and for those who follow. I danced for those who were born and those who would die. I danced with the inspired abandonment of human reason. In that dank small space beneath the old house, I felt connected to a life force much greater than my own. As it was power, then powerful I had become. The heavy beats of the celestial *pahu* thundered mightily in the dark night and for the first time ever in my life, I danced *kahiko* from the very depths of my being.

When the dance ended, my body was covered with a thin sheen of perspiration that glistened in the soft glow of moonlight. I felt an admiration in the tender fingers of that moonlight reaching toward me through the diamond spaces of the latticework. I felt it caress my shoulders, my chest, the engorged muscles in my thighs. Exhausted, I moved into the far corner of the low space, towards the rear of the old house. In the soft, soothing mud, I lay down on my side, breathing *uh-uh-uh* contentedly, as the rain dripped down the outside of the house.

I slept soundly through the night.

The next evening I went over to Cassandra's. I wanted her help in trying to understand what was happening to me. As I approached in the jeep, the three big dogs roared off the porch, barking and snarling. They attacked the tires of the vehicle ferociously, snapping with their bare teeth at the door handle and window. The Akita jumped from the ground and up to the partly opened passenger window of the jeep. He hung partially through the window, snarling and snapping, his fangs bared and muzzle frothing. The thick hair on the back of my neck stood on end and I snarled in return, spraying the dashboard with saliva. I struck at him mightily with my right fist, crashing against the top of his skull and hammering his neck into the edge of the raised glass. The glass shattered. The dog was immediately silenced, shards of broken glass cutting into his jugular vein and vocal chords. Thick blood pulsed from his neck, running in rivulets down the inside of the door. He was still scrabbling with his rear legs, trying to gain purchase, when I yanked the steering wheel to the left and he fell heavily from the window. I felt the rear tire hit solidly, as it rolled completely over him. Beneath the surge of the engine, I heard the crunch of his ribcage. I quickly sped away.

I called Cassandra later from a pay phone at the village.

"Cassandra, I'm sorry," I said.

"Don't come back here anymore, EVER!" she screamed. "Stay away. You stay away!"

She slammed the phone down. In the drizzling rain, I listened to the dial tone and wondered what had become of my life.

It was unusually cold that evening. I turned on the light and looked at myself in the mirror. I used to think of myself as an attractive man, but I could no longer hold this belief. My beard was thick and bristly. My lateral incisors and canine teeth had elongated. The shape of my head was somehow protracted and my nose – well I'm not sure what that looked like, I couldn't see it anymore, my eyes were filled with tears. "Dear God," I thought. "What is happening to me?"

I lit a fire in the small fireplace and watched the sparking embers snap from the damp 'ōhi'a logs. I lay on my side on the floor and struggled to understand the feelings that tormented me. Was it love that I feared the most? The unequivocal devotion of one being to another? I remembered the feeling of moonlight glistening on the pectoral muscles of my chest. Was this the love of an entity outside of my own world? Something more powerful than I could possibly imagine? I chewed on a piece of 'awa root, enjoying the gritty taste of dirt on the small roots. The 'awa numbed my gums and lips. I held the pulp on my tongue savoring the dry, wooden taste. I was losing hold of all that I had ever been, I thought, staring into the embers of the crackling fire.

Magically, the burning sparks rose in the wall of flames and spelled out:

You are loved by me, my Kama
Beautiful as the lehua blossom

That night, I chanted in the soft moonlight and smacked my thin, black lips. I danced, *'ai ha'a*, beneath the wooden floor of the small cottage until my legs were leaden and my ankles were weak from exertion. Again, I felt her embrace in the deep darkness, as she favored me with silk, shreds of *lehua*, and tiny fragments of fresh, white ginger. These tender ministrations of sweet *aloha* eased the loneliness in my heart. The ache that had haunted me for so many years was finally gone. For the first time since the death of my parents did I again feel loved. I closed and ended the *kahiko* and my tears fell, streaming through the coarse, black hair of my face. The world I had believed in for so many years, a world of rational thought, governed by the rules of scientific logic, was finally proven to be an illusion. It became clear to me that I had created my life from a false and vain intellectualism. The antiseptic world I fashioned was never able to fill even the smallest vacancy in my heart. My useless paradigm had failed. I felt relieved to let it go. I felt joy in its release. I felt it leave my chest and fly upward through the old wooden floor. I knew that a door to the past had closed, and that a new and mysterious one had to some extent, opened. I could see it in my mind as clearly as I could see my own hands, the fierce red light streaming from within. I lowered my head and placed my palms on the outside of that door. I squared my shoulders, dug my feet into the thick *lepo* and grunted forcefully into the waning starlight. The strength that flowed through my spine seemed inhuman. I pushed mightily and prepared my heart for a new beginning.

I awoke to the sound of crunching gravel. Through the lattice, I could see the National Park Emblem on the door of the gray pickup truck coming down the driveway. I noticed at the end of the clearing that several *'apapane* birds had flown out of the green forest and had gathered on the telephone wire. The truck was coming closer. More and more of the *'apapane* arrived. The truck braked in front of the house. The little birds began to chirp, to squawk and flutter their wings, trilling in the cool morning air. There were several dozen of them and more arriving as the truck door opened. Disembodied legs in pressed khaki pants swung down and marched towards the steps. It could only be Drakes, his fancy leather shoes moving towards my hiding place beneath the house. I could barely repress a deep, almost unconscious snarl as I heard him come up the mossy wooden steps of the porch. The *'apapane* were quite agitated now. They had completely filled the telephone wire. They landed in large numbers on the roofline of the house and flew over to the rafters of the small open garage. They squawked in the adjacent trees, trilling louder and louder. Drakes pounded on the wooden door, nervously noticing the birds all around him.

"Weir!" he hollered. "Weir!"

I struggled not to make a sound. All of a sudden, the 'apapane became very quiet, hundreds of them tilting their heads and leaning forward from their perches, looking menacingly down at Drakes. In their enormous numbers, the sight was intimidating.

"Damn!" he muttered, backing up and looking around at them. He proceeded to walk very slowly back to the truck. He quietly opened the door. When he felt he was safe from the birds, he slammed the door of the truck and started the engine, revving it and spraying dirt and gravel from the rear wheels of the vehicle. The 'apapane exploded from their perches, screaming insanely. A dark cloud of angry birds swirled around the departing vehicle, their small, black wings furiously beating the air. The sound of their exclamations carried through the forest, shattering the quiet calm of the morning.

At work, a few days later, Drakes abruptly pulled up a chair to face me across from my desk.

"Look, Weir, I'll tell you right now, you are in serious trouble. I'm fed up with your irregular hours and your damned disrespectful attitude. I'm simply not going to put up with it anymore." He laced his fingers together and leaned forward on my desk. I was snacking on whole macadamias from a paper bag. I had discovered that I could crush the hard outside shell with my teeth. I spat the broken pieces into the bag and relished the sweet, oily nut. I chewed the raw nut and swallowed slowly, looking silently at Drake.

"Weir, how many volcanologists would give their gonads to have your job? Do you have any idea?" he raised his voice sharply. "Your productivity is down and your illusory problems with the computers are wasting time. Nicholas can't protect you anymore, Weir, he's gone. Maybe we should get a volcanologist who wouldn't waste time with moronic cultural pap and actually accomplish some real science. I'm seriously thinking about letting you go, Weir. Perhaps selling leis down at the airport would be more suited to your temperament."

There was silence between us that thickened like the mist in the adjacent crater. I spit more sharp pieces into the bag and looked at Drakes' self-satisfied, sadistic smile. I noticed the message displayed on my computer monitor. I smiled back at Drakes. The screen said simply:

Bring him to me, my beloved

I felt a quiver run down my spine and looked down at my left forearm on the support of the chair. The hair was thick and coarse, extending from the back of my hand up beneath the sleeve of my shirt.

"Look Drakes," I said hesitantly, "I apologize for the irregularities." I put the paper bag down on the desk. "I'm struggling with my dissertation and having some difficulties finishing up. I'd appreciate one more chance. Come with me to take a look at Halema'uma'u later this afternoon. It will explain everything."

Drakes looked at me and considered this. "What's in it for me, Weir? You going to make me a nice *lei* too?"

He smiled thinly. I pushed my chair back. Drakes' arrogant cynicism was disturbing but not as disturbing as the scent emanating from his body. The man smelled awful.

"This discovery will make an impressive addition to the field data in your monthly administration reports. You can have all the credit. You'll be lauded for this finding, Drakes . . . could be they'd even consider better funding for your position."

He considered this new angle for another moment. "You'd better be right, Weir," Drakes said sullenly, "and clean this damn crap off your desk."

He pushed his arm across the desk, knocking the paper bag of macadamia shells to the floor. He rose stiffly and returned to his office.

I picked up the phone a minute later and called him. "Drakes, we should be as discreet as possible. You know how competitive it can get around here, we don't want to tip our hand. Let's wait until everybody else has left, then we can go out to the crater together. I'd like the credit to go exclusively to you Drakes, not Marshals or Lane. Perhaps you could sign out when we leave, and I'll come back up and sign out later. It might be less suspicious if I wasn't officially with you when you log the finding."

"Weir, if this is a waste of my time, it will mean your termination," he said ominously and hung up.

I typed into the system:

WHO ARE YOU?

After a few seconds, the swirling green phosphors came to life.

It is I, ke ahi, who loves you

I looked out the window of the observatory. The sun was setting over Mauna Loa, deep streaks of crimson giving way to the cool turquoise blues of an early twilight. I removed a small bottle of gin from the bottom drawer of my filing cabinet. I joined Drakes in the parking lot and looked around to be sure that we were not observed. We drove down the Chain Of Craters road, then I parked the jeep off to the side, near a thick jumble of ferns. We began to walk. On our way out to the crater, I went over to one of the steam vents and knelt over the sparkling yellow crystals that coated the rocks of the opening. I inhaled deeply. The sulfur felt so good in my nostrils.

"Can you hear that?" I asked Drakes, as he approached curiously.

"Hear what?" Drakes replied.

"The chanting," I said, studying the vent. "It's coming from below, beneath the molten lava."

"What?" Drakes said. He couldn't hear me, as the vent began to hiss. His eyes narrowed and he looked at me suspiciously.

We hiked a little further in the gathering darkness.

"This way, Drakes, we're almost there," I said. We lay on our bellies, inching forward. I leaned over carefully to observe the inconceivable vista of the fiery pit beneath us. The crater was beautiful in the fading light, bubbling and boiling, roiling in phosphorescent pinks, reds and oranges. Drakes was coming up beside me, very afraid; I could smell the stink on him. "She's down there," I whispered in veneration, feeling the hardness of my *kano* digging into the earth. Drakes' trembling hand reached for the edge of the crater rim. Slowly he pulled himself towards the edge. I reached into my back pocket for the fifth of gin, unscrewed the cap and took a long swig.

"Drakes," I said, looking down into a sea of molten lava. "I don't think I'd enjoy selling *leis* at the airport. I like it here, engaged in my work. In fact, I've recently discovered a completely new aspect to volcanology. It's the radically transformative idea that nothing is really what we think it is, Drakes . . . . Nothing."

I extended my arm and released the bottle down into the deep abyss. There was a tinkling sound, way, way down there as the glass shattered.

I stood evenly on the crater rim and began *ka 'olili* – the shimmering. Drakes jumped to his feet and started to run, but he moved awkwardly in his leather shoes. Mine were already off, the nails of my toes, joining, as if hoofed. Drakes had run about thirty yards, but I cut off his escape easily. I moved in towards him relishing the smell of his fear. He stumbled backwards, holding up his hands and pleading with me. His voice was small and timid. I ran my tongue across my lips. He backed up to the edge of the crater where he could go no further.

I dropped down to all fours.

"My God," he whimpered, releasing the smell of urine into the air.

I bellowed joyously, flying over the rocks to slam my face into the soft flesh of his pelvis. The muscles in my neck strained mightily as I flung him upwards with my head. Drakes went over the cliff backwards, screaming all the way to the fiery bottom.

When he hit the molten pond, the upward splash of lava threw shimmering strands of liquefied fire into the cool night air. She was indeed a goddess. In her own incredible *'olili*, her glorious red eyes burned in the darkness. Pele smiled, beckoning, her radiant splendor without comparison. Above the seething caldera, the smell of burnt flesh rose. Sniffing at the twisting smoke and dancing *'ai ha'a* along the rim, I was fulfilled to the center of my being.

When the full moon came out from behind the clouds, the *'olili* finally solidified. I chanted vibrantly into the heavenly darkness —

He miki, he miki
A i hānau mai 'oe e Hina
Ka maka o ka pua'a
E lele ana i ka lani
E lele ana i ke kuahiwi
'Ewalu maka o ke keiki pua'a a Hina

I ran like the wind: powerful, low. My beastly hooves struck the ground, pulverizing and smashing the *pāhoehoe* into dirt. In the cold breath of the *'ena makani*, dust from my swift passage floated upwards and away beneath the purple starlight. I inhaled the volcanic spores of her essence, her beauty flooding my senses. Cloaked in the dark cape of night, I raced forward to the promise of her womanhood.

Behold *Kamapua'a*, lover of the Fire Goddess.

＊ ＊ ＊ ＊ ＊ ＊ ＊ ＊ ＊ ＊

When the ambulance stops, they transport me on the gurney to the operating table. The nurses attach electrodes to my chest. I can see the monitor off to the side of the surgeon. Beep, beep, beep. The data dissolves and the dancing blue cathode rays declare her sweet epistle:

Return to me soon, beloved

Her message is visible only for an instant, for a single heart beat, then the screen returns to the normal output of the cardiac display.

It seems quite fitting, that the woman I love so passionately speaks within the beating of my own heart. The anesthesiologist frowns above his mask and raps gently on the side of the screen. I am smiling, my eyes shining in the bright lights of the operating theater.

It is so good to be loved. The anesthetic begins to take effect. I close my eyes as the surgeon leans forward to irrigate and repair the wound. As he enters and tugs at my flesh, I recall her gentle caress. The smell of her hair. The incredible taste of her warm mouth. The way I parted her thighs with the movement of my dark snout. This was not the love I had hoped for in my life. It was more. So much more.

The next morning, I look in the mirror of the bathroom and see my face. Miraculously, I am handsome again and I feel good. I raise the hospital gown and examine the wound. There is no pain. The stitches are secure. The healing has commenced.

In a few days, I will wear my flannel shirt and drink a cup of *mamaki* tea. I will read the Hilo Tribune and back up the seismic data on the big drives. I open the hospital window and inhale the soft, sweet scent of vog. It is the most delicate of perfumes.

For now, I am hungry. I roam the kitchen early, before any of the staff arrive. I find a carton of eggs.

One by one, I place them in my mouth.

Author's Note:

The demi-god Kamapua'a had two principal forms: human being and that of a hog. According to the Kumulipo creation chant, he was born in the fifth era. I was engaged in the production research for the show "'Ulalena" on Maui, when I came upon a reference in the Fornander Collection of Hawaiian Antiquities and Folklore first published in 1918–1919 by The Bishop Museum Press in Honolulu as "Memoirs of Bernice Pauahi Bishop Museum of Polynesian Ethnology and Natural History, Vol. V, Parts I, II and III." What stunned me was a mysterious reference in the text, a description of Kamapua'a as "ka haole nui maka 'ālohilohi – the large foreigner with the bright eyes." I had to put down my pen and think about this. Then I began to wonder what would happen, if after all this time, Pele longed for her old lover?

All chant references in this story except for "Aia Lā 'O Pele" are from the Fornander Collection of Hawaiian Antiquities and Folklore, Volume V, Part II pg. 314–363. The facsimile edition (text pages) was published in 1999 by 'Ai Pohaku Press, 1244 North School Street, Honolulu, HI 96817. "Aia Lā 'O Pele" is from the Beamer family collection.

HOʻI HOU I KA MOLE
Kahi Brooks

I admit that
Sometimes I wonder
what they would think of me
Would they see me
pale, blue jeans, Frappucino
and find me more foreign than haole
My Ford more strange than the *Endeavor*,
or would they see me
(Tūtū can you see me?!)
and know me as their own
koko, ʻiwi, moʻokūʻauhau

And everytime I wonder
every time I ask, they answer
Moʻo, they say, there is
nothing to know
you are the skin wrapped
around our bones
We are the spine
holding up your body
we are as rain and a running stream
the same, unable to
exist without each other.
And yet, they say, it is
you that struggles to recognize us.
We are all around you
listen—without trying, hear your own
koko, ʻiwi, moʻokūʻauhau
and understand that you belong to us.

(Epilogue)
Every time I hear them
their answer, their reassurance,
their fact.
I am dumbfounded by the
oppressed victim
lurking in my own mind
(in plain sight!)
it frightens me,
fills me with distrust
for my thoughts, for my feelings

so I take a deep breath
and force myself
force myself
to listen without trying,
to hear my own
koko, ʻiwi, moʻokūʻauhau
and be at peace

OPEN IT!
Richard Hamasaki

Like a tin can
beer bottle
closet door
combination lock
sealed letter

      open it —
      open the can
      open the bottle

      open the door
      open the safe
      open your mind

Open it up
open it a crack
pry it open

Open it even though it wants to close
Open it even though it wants to sleep
Open it even though it refuses to listen

      you cover your ears!
      you cover your eyes!
      you cover your mouth!
      — you cover yourself!

Are you hungry?
open your mind
Are you weak?
open your mind

Are you tired?
open your mind
Are you desperate?
open your mind

Are you angry?
open your mind
Are you bitter?
open your mind

> open your mind — it's like cans of fish
> open your mind — it's like endless bottles of beer
> open your mind — it's a very dark closet
> open your mind — it's a combination of locks
> open your mind — it's like opening a letter
> opening your mind

opening your mind
opening your mind
opening your mind

KE ALA ʻILIʻILI O HĀLOA

John Noah P. Hoʻomanawanui

Here I sink my feet into the soil of generations past
It soothes my core, my inner truth
After miles of walking and acquiring foreign sediments
I am taken back to a path less travelled
  through an ocean-like field of fertile soil and conscious
  movement

Here I know the islands are my ancestral home
While there I am fed my ancestors' bones
Too bitter to chew, too hard to swallow
They try to shape me into something I cannot be,
into someone besides *me*, he Hawaiʻi

Here I am Hawaiian, carrying the koko and kuleana of
ancestors past
There I am a novelty, entertaining to the eye —
epistemologically, just a pre-school lullabye
There I am not taken seriously, just tested and fitted into a category
But I have my own mind, heart, and voice —
My soul belongs to my people — not by choice, but by birth,
One with those planted in the soil, the soothing embrace of
  Papahānaumoku!

Here the voices in the wind strengthen me
They guide and correct me
There I am metaphorically sliced in two —
Intentionally? Yes! And in a congenial manner to boot!
There I have no mind, heart, or voice.
They think that if it is academic, it's not of my conception
but borrowed — or even stolen — in their minds
No, they won't dare speak it — but it's in the eyes

Here, I am given chances time after time,
from missed prayers and forgotten protocols
The wind does not dissect me with hurricane force
Instead it blows forgiveness over the soul,
through my trespasses on the glories of Wākea

There I am considered *stuck* in the mud,
stagnate and without thought for the future
Incarcerated in Hālawa and in society
Held captive to their truths, their standards

Here I am with my people,
Moving forward by looking back
Here, I am with my older sibling, Hāloa,
in our loʻi ʻohana, the taro patch!

CULTURE BLIND

Holo Hoʻopai

Lanakila

This summer my family and I are going camping at Kaʻili Sands. This beautiful black sand beach is at the end of a long, narrow dirt road that is hidden by an overgrowth of *naupaka* plants.

Like every other year before this, my father leaves *kalo* and *ʻuala* wrapped in *ti* leaves on the side of a large boulder. This odd-shaped boulder resembles a *manō*, the shark, our family *ʻaumakua*. He is asking the beach to allow us to stay and to keep us safe. This tiresome ritual seemed so pointless to me. My mind wanders and I soon visualize myself driving around town. I would much rather be at home, but my mother forced me here.

As soon as we set up camp, my father calls to me from the shore. "Lanakila!" he yells. "It's time to catch *puhi*." I dash towards the shore in excitement. When I got there I saw that my father had quietly walked onto the reef, net in hand. He said in the gentlest voice, "Come on son."

Over the crashing of the waves I screamed, "Dad! Are we going fishing now?"

He quickly turned his head and stared at me with such a look that was so frightening it made me want to run. I didn't have the slightest idea of what I had done wrong but I knew something was wrong. He hastily threw his net onto his shoulder and walked back ashore in disbelief.

I dropped to the sand and gazed at the sunset. The lava red sky brought temporary relief to my tangled thoughts. I heard the sound of the sand shooting up into the air coming closer to me. The sound stopped right beside me and my father sat beside me.

He said, "Son, if we say we will catch fish, the fish will hear us and swim away. Even though I said that we were going to catch *puhi*, what I really meant was that we will catch fish. Since the *puhi* heard me, they all scattered to hide underneath rocks. They wouldn't eat the fish or disturb us while we would go netting. Do you understand, son?"

Malino

I had to force my son, Lanakila, to come with us to Kaʻili Sands. He's getting older and about to leave the nest. I always remind him to pay attention while his father speaks!

It saddens me to see his lack of interest in his own culture. It seems odd though, his younger brother, Kama, loves to talk Hawaiian with *tūtū* and his sister, Nāpua, is deep in the art of hula. Lanakila has steered himself away from all of this.

My husband, Kīlohi, came walking to the tent. He started speaking of how Lanakila never pays attention to what he says and how Lanakila is blind to his own culture.

"He cares more about his shoes than his own culture. I have been trying to teach him how to cast the net since he was born. He never listens to a word that I say. Every year, with him, it's like I'm teaching a new and different person how to fish!"

"Kīlohi, have some patience. Lanakila is trying very hard to learn what he can. This will probably be the last time that he spends with us here. Don't do this here — now!"

Lanakila

I awoke to the sound of the ocean. After breakfast, I took a stroll on the beach. With the cool breeze flowing across my body as I walked, all I could think about was the beauty of the sea and the magnificent colors in the sky. Then I unexpectedly felt as if my head was possessively turned to face the ocean. As the cool wind surrounded my face it whispered, "Beware of the ocean." My eyes seemed focused on one particular area in the ocean where it was calm. Then out of nowhere a white tip fin split the surface of the sea. It was a *manō*. I ran to camp and asked my mother where Nāpua and Kama were. When she told me that they were playing on the sand, like a bullet I ran to the water's edge. Without any explanation I grabbed both of them and dragged them to the tent.

I asked my mother where Dad was. My mother, now confused and startled at my actions, answered, "I . . . I think he's out on the reef." I ran as fast as my legs could carry me down to the reef.

When I got to the edge of the shore I looked for him on the reef. I looked to my right and then to my left as far as I could see. I saw nothing but rocks. I looked in front of me and my eyes seemed to just stare at one area of the ocean where the water was calm. Again, a fin split the surface of the sea. I looked down to my feet where something was now resting on them. I saw my father's fishing net. I picked it up and pulled. It felt as if it had caught an entire island. I summoned all of my strength and with one heave, the net came splashing towards the rocky shore. Too shocked to move, I just stood there with one side of the net still in my hand. My mother saw this and ran down to where I was. She grabbed my father and tried to untangle him from his own net. She gave out a ghostly scream that shook my insides as she wailed.

Lanakila

After my father's ashes were sent out to sea at Ka'ili Sands, I went and sat there on that very same spot where I had won the tug-of-war with the ocean for my father. I yelled out to the ocean, "You took my father!" I didn't know who I was yelling at — the seas for making my father lose his balance on the reef, the net which entangled him and pulled him under, or maybe myself, for not being able to say goodbye to him.

I ended up staying in that very spot until the sun was well beneath the surface of the sea. I watched the ocean as it rose and fell with the coming of larger waves. I watched the colors of the sky change from light blue, to orange, to purple, to pink, then to navy blue.

I couldn't believe that he is really gone. He is gone as well as his valuable teachings. There is nothing that I could learn from him now. Guilt and regret settled in me. I wished now that I had just tried to learn from him. If I had just paid a little more attention to what he was trying to tell me, I would have known more about him and about our own culture. If I had cared a little more, I would have realized that he was giving a piece of himself to me. Now it was too late. When my father was living, so did his skills and knowledge. When my father died, so did his skills and knowledge.

KAHAKAI

Hina Kahanu

At kahakai, the beach,
where I gathered these shells for you
I thought about how your dad
and I had talked about the hand-holding
between grandparents and grandchildren
that can save a language.
A bridge across "the generation born with no ears."

I tell my students, What good writing is about is:
it's about good thinking.
Ho'oipo said, My friends are too intense.
I think about that.

Pua said, I've felt like
jumping up on the big koa conference table and
machine-gunning all the people at the table
for what they've done to Hawaiian people.
But I do the harder thing;
I hold them with aloha.

Against my left wrist I feel
Kupuna Kauahipaula's fingertips insisting
I learn to answer her "Pehea 'oe?"
"Maika'i," she says. "Maika'i," I repeat.
"Maika'i, mahalo," she says. "Maika'i, mahalo," I say.
She releases the firmness of her grip
on my wrist.
My pulse beats stronger,
her mana.
I am held
in her aloha.
Her hold, now
a caress.

ISLAND GIRL

Lisa Linn Kanae

On the cover of the Royal Hawaiian
Shopping Center brochure,
a girl wears a crown of yellow plumeria
tilted slightly forward -
grazes the top of her eyebrows.
Straight black hair
frames her airbrushed face.

During the photo shoot,
in the photographer's backyard,
Bach's Air in the Key of G
floats over tripods and wardrobe racks.
Silver umbrellas filter ten o'clock sunlight.
She wears plaid boxer shorts
beneath a borrowed red pareau.
Between costume changes she studies
prerequisite world history 151, while
the stylist retouches her blush,
reapplies glue to an uncooperative eyelash.

The girl's features are not Asian,
Caucasian, or Pacific Islander.
More like the "other" on a census form.
A face without allegiance to one ethnicity,
ad agency exotic: one print hits
more than two marketing targets.

After the photo shoot,
she catches the number 47, Waikiki
gets off at the coffee shop
between Kalakaua Avenue and Lewers Street.
She enters the women's restroom
before the dinner rush,
changes into a kapa-print uniform to
greet three hundred guests, two to six at a time.

She hands each person a dinner menu
printed in English and Japanese.

Tonight's special —
Try our authentic Hawaiian Pineapple Boat
when you order a Porter House steak with
French fries or rice.

Behind the cashier's counter she
slips coupons inside cocktail menus;
One free continental breakfast
with every twenty-five dollar purchase.

LESSON OF ESSENCE (RECESS II)
Kealoha

I was coming out of the ocean
Approaching the showers minding my own biz
When I met this kid

He must have been 'bout one to two
Walking but not talking yet
Completely naked
Skin soon to be brown
But as of now completely unexposed

So he looks at me and I look
Back
He stares intently as the red rubber ball in my hands all wide-eyed
And I'm like "oh, you want this ball?"

He immediately grabs it bounces it and giggles
He just tickled his own imagination
And I continue on with my biz
Shower up as if
To say hey . . . you go play with that ball for a bit . . .
He runs off his momma calls to him
"Makana, be careful"
And I'm thinking to myself Makana means 'gift'

And I continue on with my biz
But this kid is captivating me
He's expressing pure joy without words as he hurls the ball
With all his might
I keep him in my sight
As sand swishes off my feet
And now I'm double, no no triple rinsing my hair which I never
        really do but I'm doing all
That I can to stall
I just want him to experience that ball

By the fifth rinse it's time for me to go
And I know it's gonna be difficult for me to get that ball back

But he throws it to me
Appreciative of the time
And at this point I'm having a very hard time leaving
So I roll the ball back
He picks it up
Bounces it for a sec
Then checks it back to me

It now seems as if we've got game
So I stay
And we play
Back and forth
Back forth
Back and forth for a bit but
Then he stops,
Drops the ball
It rolls off
And he holds out his hand

I go get the ball
Then I go to give him five
But realize
That that's not what he's trying to communicate

He looks sad . . .
Or in pain, yeah that's it it's pain
'Cause I now see a poki pricking into his finger
I barely even touch it but he reacts automatically
Shudders dramatically
And yet he still stands
With his hand out
He trusts me with this poki

So I'm thinking . . .
I've gotta do this quick otherwise
We're both in deep doo-doo
'Cause his skin is like tissue
It's ridiculously sensitive
And pokis...they *freaking* hurt, y'all!!

And his eyes
Are peering into mine
With pure trust
You see
He hasn't yet been
Sworn into a childhood
Of "don't talk to strangers they're dangerous villains out to get you"
He hasn't had time
To learn how to ignore
The rest of his community as his day passes by
He hasn't learned this societal nonsense
He's simply being as his heart tells him to be

Trusting . . . of me

He's open and standing
And I'm asking
His momma who's five feet away . . .
"Is it okay?"

She smiles and nods yes
She gives me the go-ahead
And so I go
I take a deep breath
And in one swift move
I grab and pull
Simultaneously
His body twitches temporarily
But the worst is now over

He looks and smiles
And I nearly cry

This is the essence of existence
He picks up the ball as if
To play again
But our time has come to an end
And my new friend
Is wondering where I'm
Wandering to
As I walk away slowly saying
"Makana, you can have the ball . . ."

And for me,
It was a small price to pay
For a brief lesson of essence

I COME TO THE WATER

Jonathan Kamakawiwo'ole Osorio

I come to the water, a child, to gather
the life and the strength of the sea
I come to the water to gather with others
For the water will not come to me
though we both, for the moment, are free

I come to the water, a young man, a lover
the pride and the hope of my family
I come to the water to sing and to wonder
And I yearn for a glimpse of my destiny
as I sail in the arms of the sea

I come to the water an elder, a father
the life and the strength of my family
I come with the others to gather and struggle
and I toil with a tiring urgency
for the children depending on me

I come to the ocean, an old man's devotion
alone with my songs and my memories
I come to the ocean and drift with emotions
for the people who've parted from me
as I nod and dream like the sea

PUA MANA NŌ
(SURE A POOR MAN)

from Mary Kawena Pukui
edited and translated by Mary Kawena Pukui and Alfons L. Korn

I

I Kahiki au i ka 'imi dālā,
    Dālā pohō.
A holo mau ma ka 'ō koholā,
    Koholā lalau.
Ua pau ku'u moku i kāhi kenekoa,
Ua pau ku'u moku i kāhi kenekoa.
Ho'i mai au he pua mana nō,
Ho'i mai au he pua mana nō.

II

I Ke-kaha au i ka ma'au'auwā,
    I ka ma'au 'auwā.
Puehu ka lepo, welawela ka lā,
    Welawela ka lā.
Ua pau ku'u pono i ka luna 'auhau,
Ua pau ku'u pono i ka luna 'auhau.
Ho'i mai au he pua mana nō,
Ho'i mai au he pua mana nō.

III

Nonoke au i ka mahi kō,
    I ka mahi kō.
Ua 'eha ke kua, kakahe ka hou,
    Pohō, pohō.
A 'ai'ē au i ka hale kū'ai,
A 'ai'ē au i ka hale kū'ai.
A noho ho'i he pua mana nō,
A noho ho'i he pua mana nō.

IV

A ha'alele au i ka 'imi dālā,
    Dālā pohō.
E noho nō e hana ma ka lā,
    Ka 'ai o ka lā.
Iā ha'i ka waiwai e luhi ai,
Iā ha'i ka waiwai e luhi ai.
E noho au he pua mana nō,
E noho au he pua mana nō.

Sure a Poor Man

I

I went to a foreign land to work for money,
    Wasted money.
Then I went to harpoon whales,
    Worthless whales.
My ship soon belonged to a senator,
My ship soon belonged to a senator.
I came home a poor man,
I came home a poor man.

II

In Ke-kaha I worked as a peddler,
    A peddler was I.
The dust blew up, the sun scorched,
    The sun did scorch and burn.
The tax collector took all my gain,
The tax collector took all my gain.
I came home a poor man,
I came home a poor man.

III

I labored on a sugar plantation,
    Growing sugarcane.
My back ached, my sweat poured,
    All for nothing.
I fell in debt to the plantation store,
I fell in debt to the plantation store.
And remained a poor man,
And remained a poor man.

IV

I decided to quit working for money,
    Money to lose.
Far better work day by day,
    Grow my own daily food.
No more laboring so others get rich,
No more laboring so others get rich.
Just go on being a poor man,
Just go on being a poor man.

A NOTE ON THE TEXT

The song is modeled on the subject matter and stanzaic structure, with prominent refrain, of American work-ballads and marching songs, especially those in the form of autobiographical narrative mixed with social protest. Pua Mana Nō, 'Sure a Poor Man,' *was written to the tune of* When Johnny Comes Marching Home. *The allusion to the "plantation store" may have been a relatively late addition to the song in its earliest version.*

‘OHANA

THIRTY CALIBRE
Adam Campbell

The sun shone brightly toward the east as it started to settle in the west. I lay on the freshly mowed grass, the bare skin of my back feeling the sharp poking of the short blades. The ground was moist, full of brown and yellow leaves from the monkey pod tree that reached about thirty feet into the air. To the right of me there grew seven rows of ti leaves flourishing in the hot sun, while to the left were tall red gingers growing formally, each plant having its own leafy, dark red flower in the center.

Uncle Charley stood on the cemented floor of the pig pen with a steel fence around it and a rectangular dome on top. "Eh, boy, go get me my knife from da truck for cut da pig. Stay in da sheath in da compartment. Eh, and no forget to close da door, uh?"

Uncle never really talked to me as if I were his young nephew. He always talked to me as though I knew everything already, as if I was as old as one of his friends. Uncle was shooting down the cemented area now, hosing off all the waste that lay there. I started to get up and a body came towards me from behind. The wide image startled me as I turned my head quickly toward the moving shadow. A huge man asked, "Ho! What *you* doing here?"

"Who's dat!" I said. "Oh, das you, Bull!" I was relieved. "I thought you wen go surf with the boys."

"Nah, I wanted for come see your brada."

"Oh!" I said. I was glad to see my cousin. He was the best cousin I had. He sat down on the green grass with his faded blue jeans and his "blown" Town and Country surf shirt full of little holes on the front.

"I thought Ted was supposed to go with Uncle," he said as he put his hand under his head, lying down on the green grass.

"Yeah, Ted was supposed to go with Uncle, but he had to go to school today."

"Oh," Bully said. "Brah, then *you* betta watch out for Uncle. Sometimes he get mad real fast."

"Yeah, I know," I said. "I goin' get Uncle's pig knife. I come back before he get mad. You know Hawaiians, yeah?"

"Wait," Bully said. I was just getting up, dusting off all the leaves from my body when Bully showed me the knife. "I brought it from the truck when I was coming here."

"Aw, nah! Right on! How you knew?" I said as I grabbed the sheath with the knife in it and thanked my cousin.

"Eh, I knew. Shoots, I gotta go already. My fada goin' bus' me if I don't come back fast. I told him I was goin' drop something off at Uncle Charley's house. 'Kay den, check you guys out later."

Bully got up and walked away. "Ka'ahele," he called over his shoulder. "No forget, da first time is da hardest."

"What?" I yelled at him.

Bully stopped and turned around. "I said, 'Da first time is da worst.'"

I stared at him.

"Forget it," he said, turning and walking away.

I went over to Uncle as he was rolling up the green garden hose. Uncle gave me a hard look. He never talked to me. All he did was point at things, and I would have to understand, or he'd yell at me.

Uncle Charley dropped the hose outside the pen. His wrinkled face and body moved quickly around, trying to catch a particular pig. He pointed to his gun under the banana tree. I ran there, grabbed it, and took it to him. By now Uncle had the pig cornered in the pen. He held a long, pointed stick to keep the screaming pig pinned in the corner. I gave Uncle the .30 calibre rifle, but he pushed it back at me. "You shoot'um," he said. I looked at him with amazement. He repeated it: "You shoot'um, I said!"

The pig was squealing louder and louder. Uncle kept poking him with the sharp stick, pushing him back and back. The sound of the screams echoed in the valley. I started to shake at the cries of the animal. I held the heavy .30 calibre and opened the chamber while Uncle handed me the brass bullet. It was so noisy I was getting more and more confused.

I tried aiming the gun at the pig's head. Then I dropped the gun gently to the concrete floor. I couldn't do it.

"Shoot'um!" he ordered, even louder, as his face turned red from heated anger.

I picked up the gun, stood it gently in the corner, and walked away.

Uncle Charley kept screaming at me: "Get back here and shoot'um, I told you!"

I could still hear him yelling, but I just kept on going. I couldn't go back.

Uncle died last year. He left me his .30 calibre.

NAWAI THE NET MAKER
Caroline Curtis

"Wait for me, Noe! I'm coming with you," Kaiki hurried up the trail that led past the taro patch and toward the upland. Noe did not stop and Kaiki was panting when he joined him. "What is the matter?" he asked as soon as he could speak. "You look as fierce as a warrior going to battle, Noe, marching along and shaking your stick."

The trail rounded a thick clump of sugar cane before it crossed the stream. Here some pigs were rooting. "Go on," shouted Noe, striking one pig and then another with his stick. "You can't stop here! Get across the stream, I say."

"What is the matter, Noe?" asked Kaiki again. "Why are you so angry with the pigs?" "Whose are they? Where are you driving them?"

"Clear up into the mountains!" Noe said and his voice was sharp with anger. "I don't know whose pigs they are and I don't care! They come around our house all the time. Two days ago they walked all over Mother's *kapa* which was spread to dry. Yesterday they rooted into our banana pit and ate half the bananas. And this morning!" Angry tears came to Noe's eyes. "I took down the food net to get some of the fish Father cooked yesterday and some ti root, sweet as sugar cane. I left the food just a moment, for I heard shouts and barking down at the beach. When I came back there were these pigs, and such a mess! They had spilled fish and ti and breadfruit. They had broken calabashes, smeared poi over everything and torn the food net. My father was angry and said it was my fault. I am going to drive these pigs up into the mountains."

"Get along, you brown-striped pig!" he shouted aloud, striking savagely at one that had stopped to root near a small tree.

"Don't you dare do that!" Suddenly a tall girl stood in the path before the boys, her eyes blazing. She caught Noe's stick and wrenched it out of his hand. "Don't you ever strike an animal as long as you live," she continued. "How would you like to be beaten so, right on your bare back?" For a moment, both boys thought the girl was going to strike Noe with his stick.

"Don't Maile!" Kaiki stepped quickly in front of his friend. "The pigs spoiled all Noe's food, broke the calabashes and even tore the net. We don't know whose pigs they are and we are going to drive them to the mountains."

"They are Nawai's pigs," Maile replied, "and we are going to take them home. Here's your stick." She threw her arms around the brown pig's neck and stroked it lovingly. "This one is Nawai's pet," she said. "He's used to kindness," and she looked up reproachfully at Noe.

"I wish Nawai would keep his pigs at home!" Noe's voice was sullen. "And feed them!"

"We'll ask him to," said Maile. "Go up and get the others. We've got to take them back."

Unwillingly the boys hunted out the other pigs and drove them all down the trail. Maile was a strange girl. She seldom played with others, but spent her time with animals or in the upland. She was usually quiet and gentle, but when her anger blazed all the children respected and obeyed her.

Silently the three returned to the village, driving the pigs. They found Nawai in his work yard, scraping *olona*. "We brought back your pigs," Maile told him. "They are hungry and taking other people's food."

Nawai leaned back against the tree to rest. "I forgot to feed them," he said. "Get some of the coconuts piled near my imu, break them and feed the pigs, you three," and Nawai continued scraping.

Maile led the way and soon the three were watching the pigs devour coconuts. "Nawai ought to feed his pigs himself," Noe repeated as Maile left them.

"Oh, he is working!" Kaiki laughed. "Nawai is the laziest man in this village. When he does work we must not interrupt him."

"Let's watch him then," Noe suggested. The two returned to Nawai's work yard and squatted quietly on the grass beside him.

Olona shoots had been cut in moist mountain gulches where they grew abundantly. The bark had been slit, peeled and soaked much as *wauke* bark was peeled and soaked for *kapa* making. As the two boys watched, Nawai tied moist bark to one end of a long smooth narrow board and scraped it with a turtle shell. This separated the long fibers from each other and the coarse outer bark. It was fascinating to watch the swift movement of the scraper. "Nawai's hands aren't like those of a wooden image today!" thought Kaiki remembering a remark of the overseer.

Noe had much the same thought. "I have seen other men scrape, but no one worked so well as Nawai," he said in a low voice. "I wonder if it is hard to learn?"

Nawai looked up. "Want to try?" he questioned.

"Oh yes!"

Nawai rose and stretched, then showed Noe how to sit at the end of the long board. Noe must hold the blade of the scraper against the bark. "Now scrape toward you," Nawai directed.

Noe tried. Several times the scraper moved along the creamy fibers. "I'm not doing anything," Noe said in disappointment.

"Keep on," Nawai advised, "You'll learn."

And now Noe did. Soon he was removing the dark outer bark. "Good for you!" Nawai praised. "Only I can't reach the other end," said Noe, bending over.

"I'll finish it," said Nawai. "Then Kaiki can have a turn."

But Kaiki had no success. "Does every man have to do this?" he asked as he let Noe scrape once more.

"No. This takes skill and only a few men learn."

"But many people twist cord," said Kaiki. "Keao, my aunt is learning to make cord for fish lines. She wants to do that because Malu is a fisherman. She let me try. It looks easy when Keao does it, but when I try the cord is bunchy."

"That too needs skill," said Nawai. He took several long fibers, laid them on his leg above the knee, and rolled them with the flat of his hand, making fine, smooth cord.

"You are skillful at everything!" exclaimed Kaiki admiringly. "But these fibers aren't as white as those Keao was twisting."

"The fibers I have scraped may be bleached in the sunshine, then twisted into cord. But we do not bleach fibers intended for a fish net," he added. "Often a net is dipped in sea water in which *kukui* bark has been soaked."

"To darken it?" asked Kaiki quickly. "So the fish will not see it gleam? Do you do all these kinds of work yourself, Nawai? I don't see how you get time to make your nets!"

"People give me cord of different sizes. Come into my work house."

While Noe scraped busily Nawai took Kaiki into his work house. There the boy saw a great bunch of hanging fibers. "Like a waterfall," he told himself. He saw many balls of twisted fiber. "All this for nets?" the boys asked. "Oh, Nawai, how many nets are you going to make?"

Nawai laughed. "I don't know," he replied. "People give me cord and I think about the net that I shall make. Maybe I start, but net making is slow. I stop to rest or swim or I must go with others to the upland. When I return I start another net."

Kaiki examined the balls of cord. "This is coarse and strong," he said. "You don't use this for a fish net."

"Yes." Nawai spread a half-finished net before the boy. "Sometimes fishermen use a net to capture a shark or turtle. Such a net must be very strong. And here is one for catching tiny bait fish."

"Why the cord is almost as fine as spider web!" Kaiki exclaimed, "and the mesh is very small. How do you make it even?"

"Watch," and Nawai took tools from a small covered gourd. He seated himself just inside the doorway where the light was good. Kaiki listened reverently to his prayer, then watched as Nawai's shuttle flew, knotting fine cord into small meshes.

"Noe, come!" Kaiki called. The two watched the flying shuttle as Nawai formed the mesh, measuring each opening with a tiny wooden gauge held in his left hand.

"That's enough for today," he said at last. "The light grows dim," and he rose to put away tools and net.

"See that dark cloud!" exclaimed Kaiki going out. "I'll help you carry in your things. It's going to rain."

"The rain will please the pigs," Noe said. "They like a muddy place."

"We all like coolness," Nawai answered. He had carried his scraping board and now went to look after the pigs. "This is my pet," he added, scratching the brown pig's back.

"That is the one that tore my father's net," remarked Noe. He had not forgotten his father's scolding.

"Tore the food net?" asked Nawai quickly. "Run and get it, boy. I'll mend the net. Hurry! The rain is almost here!"

Sitting inside the doorway, while the rain fell outside, Nawai mended the torn net. The boys squatted near, watching. "That is sennit you are using, and not *olona*," Kaiki remarked.

"Yes, this food net is made of coconut fiber," Nawai answered. "For fish lines and nets we use *olona* because saltwater does not rot it, and it does not kink."

"I know!" said Noe. My father told me about a net used three generations and it is still good."

"Fishermen take good care of their nets," Nawai told them.

"I should say they do!" said Kaiki. "Malu spends almost as much time drying and mending nets as he does fishing! Yesterday I wanted him to show me how to catch tiny eels, but he had to go to the chief's fishing house to mend a net."

For a long time the boys watched the net-maker's rapid work. "There!" he said at last. "Your food net is as good as new, Noe."

Noe thanked him. "Father will be pleased," he said, then added thoughtfully, "Why do we use sennit if *olona* is better, Nawai?"

"*Olona* is better in salt water," Nawai replied, "but sennit too, is good."

"And rope is made from *hau* bark," added Kaiki.

"Yes," Nawai answered, "the gods have given us many good fibers. Delicate cords of braided hair hold the neck ornaments of chiefs. With *hau* ropes we haul canoes from the upland. In house building *'uki'uki* and *'ie'ie* are used. From *olona* we make fish nets, and the net work for feather capes and helmets."

"Capes and helmets!" Noe exclaimed. "Can you make nets for those, Nawai?"

"I have never made a cape or a helmet," Nawai replied, "but I can show you what my master taught me." He searched in a large calabash and brought out a sample of the finest network the boys had ever seen. "A cape is made in this way," he explained. "The tiny feathers are knotted in, a few at a time, by an expert. A helmet is made of *'ie'ie* rootlets and closely covered with such a net."

"Oh, that's too much work!" said Kaiki. "But beautiful," Noe added slowly. "Oh, Nawai, I want to be a net maker! Will you take me as your pupil?"

Nawai looked thoughtfully at Noe. "Do you want to feed my pigs each day?" he asked. "Do you want to go with me to cut *olona* shoots and peel and scrape? Do you want to run errands and help in little ways?"

"Yes, I do," said Noe solemnly.

"Very well, help me for a time. If you work well, I'll take you as a pupil if your father likes the plan. I've tried to teach my son, but he is even lazier than I," and Nawai laughed.

"E, net maker!" Lako was calling from the yard. "The rain has stopped. Make ready to go tomorrow to the upland. The twigs of *hau* and *kukui* we put on the sweet-potato patch have rotted. They have given their strength to the field. Tomorrow the overseer commands that we go up and plant sweet-potato cuttings."

"It is always so!" muttered Nawai. "Here I have bark to scrape and nets half-finished and now I must stop to plant potatoes."

Kaiki chuckled. "Nawai is lazy!" he told himself. "But he's clever. Noe can learn much from him. As for me, I'd rather be a farmer!" and he turned a handspring as he hurried off to help Puako get ready for the upland.

HOʻOKUPU

kuʻualoha meyer hoʻomanawanui

E hō mai ka ʻike mai luna mai ē. I nā mea huna noʻeau, o nā mele ē.
E hō mai, e hō mai, e hō mai ē…

Mōhala sat on the front porch with the worn wooden cutting board placed firmly on the table in front of her, carefully cutting the hala fruit she had gathered from Tūtū's tree in the front yard. Slowly and methodically she cut the sides of each key, slicing in, and then down at an angle, just how her older brother Lehia had taught her only two years ago. She had begged him to teach her how to cut the hala into the beautiful five-point stars that were then strung with lauaʻe into long strands; tied together with ribbon it made a perfect lei. He had said she was too young to handle the sharp knife necessary to cut through the tough hard skin of the hala fruit, but Mōhala had persisted. When Lehia was cutting and stringing a hala lei for their cousin Puna's high school graduation that year, Mōhala had made a particularly passionate plea to learn. Lehia finally relented, and soon regretted it. He showed Mōhala how to hold the knife blade like a scalpel in her right hand while grasping the hala fruit with her left. "Press down and in at the same time," he had instructed her "and mai poina–the knife is sharp–watch your fingers."

Lehia had passed the old cutting board to her, the wooden one Tūtū Kepa had made from the trunk of a large mango tree. Lehia favored the wooden board because it had more grip than the new plastic ones sold in the markets. The rough wooden grain helped keep the fruit from slipping as it was being cut. As Mōhala pressed down on the ripe fruit, cutting into the fibrous flesh, the sweet fragrance was released, perfuming the air around her with its pungent scent. "Mmmm—smells good," she said, and pressed harder. Just then the knife slipped and cut through the fruit, slicing into her finger. The trickle of red mixed in with the moist yellow stains left on the board by the previously cut hala, leaving a pretty orange pattern. "Auwī!" Mōhala said dropping the knife, as she swiftly stuck the injured finger into her mouth. The knife clattered to the ground, barely missing a baby toe. Lehia laughed. "I told you—akahele!" he said as he took the board away from her. He showed her again how to do it, and then let her practice until she got it right. Oh how the tips of her fingers had ached afterwards! She didn't realize then that as she pushed the point of the blade into the resisting skin of the fruit that the back of the blade resisted, too. It pressed deeply into the sensitive tips of her young fingers, making a deep indentation. She thought of that now as she strung the sweet–smelling crimson fruit onto an old rag; key after key alternated with diamond–shaped pieces of laua'e until they made four strands long enough to reach from her neck to her waist. "Cloth mo'bettah den string," Lehia had told her, "cuz da string cuts through the soft fruit."

When she was pau she picked up four long broad ti leaves from the table and held them together by their stem, wrapping the lei around them. Then she carefully folded each leaf up and twisted the ends, tying them into a neat bundle. When the pū'olo was complete, she carried it to the kitchen and placed it in the refrigerator, alongside the ones which held the red fish Daddy had speared the day before. Aunty Aulani was standing at the stove, stirring canned corned beef and Maui onions into the sizzling hot black iron skillet. "You pau already?" She asked, as she sprinkled in the Hawaiian salt.

"Yeah," Mōhala said, rummaging through the refrigerator.

"When you goin' out?" Aunty Aulani asked, placing the poi bowl on the table.

"Tonight," Mōhala answered.

Aunty said nothing as she set Tūtū's blue tin dinner plates on the table. Mōhala counted them out in her head: one for Aunty and one for Tūtū, one for Daddy and one for Puna, one for her, and one…missing. She couldn't forget; now there was one missing.

"Goin' where?" Puna's question interrupted her thoughts. She looked up at her cousin coming in the kitchen door carrying three fat 'uhu strung to-gether on a line. Mōhala couldn't help but think that as she sat on the porch stringing hala, her cousin was a few hundred yards away in the water, spear-ing fish and stringing them together like a lei. The salt water glistened on his dark brown skin as he set the fish on the counter next to his mother.

"You like me fry 'em for dinner?" Aunty asked, as she reached for the shiny dead fish.

"Yeah, Ma," Puna replied, as he grabbed a beer from the refrigerator. "Ho, you shoulda seen da menpachi; man, had plenny! But that frickin' shark came at me again today wen' I was tryin' fo' spear 'em, an' he wen' scare me! Next time we go divin' me an' Russell folks goin' take his faddah's gun an' try shoot da bugga," Puna said, grabbing the dried 'ōpae from the cupboard. He sat at the table with Mōhala, and took a long swig of his bottled beer. "So Mo, where you goin' tonight?" he said, focusing his atten-tion on her.

"You know where I goin'," she said, returning his gaze. "To da ko'a."

Puna stared at her with a look of annoyance. "Da ko'a? Why da hell you goin' ova' dea? Ma, why you guys lettin' her go ova dea?" Puna said, turning towards his mother.

"Eh, it's her choice Puna, let her go if she like," Aunty Aulani said, as she dropped the cleaned and salted fish into the smoking hot oil.

"Da ko'a. Eh, Mo, you don' know about dat kine stuff like your braddah, no make la' dat. You goin' get hurt," Puna said, throwing a handful of 'ōpae into his mouth like popcorn.

"Eh, *I* know," Mōhala replied. "*You* da one who doesn't know." She stood up and spun around abruptly, heading out the door. She jumped down the stone steps and landed lightly on the soft grass with her bare feet, and ran towards the ocean.

"Come on Mōhala, I goin' beat you!" Lehia's laughter echoed in her mind. She remembered how they would run and chase each other down to the beach almost everyday after school since they were little children, each racing the other to be the first to dive into the cool Pacific water. "Lehia! Wait! Don't leave me!" She would cry as her little legs raced to keep up with her older brother. "I not goin' leave you, Tita," he would say, and wait for her to catch up before diving into the welcoming embrace of the sea.

The coarse pink sand crunched under foot as Mōhala reached the shore. She walked the hundred or so yards down the beach to the ko'a, the fishing stone that sat at the edge of the water in the middle of the small bay. First she had to cross the muliwai, the mouth of the small streamlet that fed into the ocean. The icy brackish water made her shiver as she stepped into the ankle–deep water. Tiny, nearly invisible fish darted around her, and long streaming limu 'ele'ele tickled her feet as she made her way across the stream. When she reached the ko'a she ran her fingers over the black stone, polished smooth from years of abuse by winds, waves, sand and salt, covering, exposing, and covering it again.

Lehia had told her about this ko'a. It was a stone altar dedicated to Kū'ulakai, the Hawaiian fishing god. "Our family 'aumakua is the manō, the shark. In the old days when someone in the 'ohana died, they would turn into a shark. Their mana would protect the rest of the family," he had told her. She hadn't believed him back then. It was just another stone on the beach; there were lots of them. How could this one be any different? She had asked Tūtū about it, hoping to prove Lehia wrong, so she could have something to tease him about. But Tūtū had confirmed his story. "When I was young," Tūtū told her, "that stone was a place for the manō to come and hānau. It was a kapu place. When people fished out here, they always went to the ko'a and left a ho'okupu on the stone. Red fish, he'e, whatever they catch. They always left the best. When the tide would rise, the rock would be completely submerged. The manō would come for the fish. Most of the time, the water there is too shallow for the sharks to swim, but when the tide is high, they can come in. They like that place to hānau, because the water is warm and calm, and there is plenty of fish because of the muliwai. That is why we don't fish there; that place is kapu to the 'aumakua."

When Tūtū was telling her this story, Puna had walked in, and laughed. "Not," he scoffed. "Tūtū, that's bulai. No such ting as shark gods, an' get plenny fish there; why gotta be kapu for some stupid sharks?" Tūtū stared at him and shook her head. She had been through this many times with Puna already. But he was stubborn, "po'o pa'akīkī," Tūtū called him; he never listened.

Puna and Lehia were first cousins and the same age. Mōhala couldn't understand how two boys the same age raised in the same house by the same family could turn out so differently. Lehia had been so proud of his Hawaiian heritage. He loved the ocean: swimming, surfing, diving, anything. Daddy used to tease him that he was a fish with legs. He loved the mountains, too. Wasn't he the one that got everyone all gung ho to go up mauka and open up the lo'i kalo? No one in the family had planted taro there in decades, not since Tūtū was a little girl. But Lehia was all for it, even though Tūtū and Daddy—and of course Puna—had complained that it was hard, backbreaking work. "Why we gotta plant taro?" Puna had complained. "Nobody like eat 'em. Me, I like rice."

"Hū, Lehia, I do' know," Daddy had said, "my body too old fo' dat kine work." But Lehia had persisted. "Why we goin' ruin our health with haole food?" Lehia asked them. "If we Hawaiians like get anywhere, we gotta help ourselves." And with that, he went mauka and started clearing and planting. Within a few days, curious neighbors stopped by to see what he was doing. "We cannot change anything unless we help ourselves. You wanna get off food stamps? Plant kalo! You wanna show your kids you somebody? Plant kalo! You want sovereignty? Plant kalo!" Lehia had told them. Soon they were working side by side in the lo'i planting huli, pulling weeds, and planning new patches. They planted bananas along the muddy banks, and sweet potatoes on the fertile slopes. They built fishponds from scrap wood and heavy plastic and experimented with raising tilapia. They met with Waiāhole and other Windward farmers to find out about their water rights, and when they discovered their water resources were being stolen in order to green leeward golf courses and urban development, they organized mass demonstrations. Within the first year, the crops were productive and demonstration successful, resulting in some water being returned to the Windward side, and everybody celebrated.

"This is jus' the first step," Lehia reminded everyone. "We gotta do more. We gotta learn our culture, and take the lead. Haoles at the HVB define Hawai'i fo' Japanese tourists. They sell our land to the highest bidder. Haoles at the University teach our language to Japanese students. Then they go teach in da DOE. What's wrong wit' us? Why we no define these things for ourselves?" he demanded. "Everyone's scared get one 'edjumacation' as Uncle Bu La'ia calls it. Why? We like dis' the Hawaiians at the University, call them 'high makamaka.' They not 'high makamaka.' We are. We da ones too vain and too scade fo' ack."

Most people had laughed him off, teasing him. "Eh braddah Le, no worries, no worries. Grab a beer an' chalang–a–lang wi'd us guys. Here, braddah, grab my 'uke. You know the one by Ka'au Crater Boys, yeah? Da 'opihi song. Yeah brah, grab a beer an' come drink wi'd us." Most people had laughed him off back then, especially Puna. "Ho cuz, why you make la' dat? Jus' kick back an' play music. No worries," Puna had said, putting his arm around his cousin's back, handing him a beer. Everyone had laughed. But not Mōhala. She had sat and listened. And not Tūtū or Daddy, either. "That boy is gonna be something one day," Daddy had said, admiring Lehia's charismatic way with a crowd, how he showed no fear when he stood up in front of them. "I sure wish I had that kind of guts when I was his age."

"Oh, you did," Tūtū replied slowly, with a distant look in her eye. "But times were different then. Who could have known things would turn out like this now?"

"What you mean, Tūtū?" Mōhala had asked, sensing an edge to Tūtū's tone of voice.

"Oh, I do'know. We were taught to be 'American,' whatever that was supposed to be. Back then it meant not speaking Hawaiian. It meant being ashamed of how you looked, of being Hawaiian. I just wanted my keiki to have the best opportunity I could give them. So I never taught them Hawaiian. I sent them to the English Standard Schools. Your Aunty, she seemed to adapt all right, but not your father. He questioned everything. But things were different back then." Tūtū had that same far away look in her eye. Mōhala followed her gaze. She was staring at Lehia.

It wasn't until the day after Lehia's speech that Mōhala had ever consciously thought about being Hawaiian. It never occurred to her before, not even all the times Lehia had tried to show her and teach her different things. "Aloha ku'u kaikuahine, ku'u hoa hānau. Pehea 'olua?" he had asked Puna and Mōhala one day as she walked in the kitchen door, straight home from classes at Windward Community College. They were sitting at the kitchen table eating sour poi and raw ʻaʻama crab seasoned with inamona.

"Huh?" Mōhala replied, wrinkling her nose at him as her teeth cracked a shiny shell.

"What da hell you said?" Puna inquired, as he slurped down some crab innards, and licked his fingers clean.

"I said, 'Aloha.' Howzit to you guys, my sistah an' cousin.' I learned dat today in my Hawaiian language class at WCC," Lehia replied. "Pretty cool, yah sis?" he asked, as Mōhala sat at the kitchen table with her mouth hanging open.

"Hawaiian language? Why you wanna take that for?" she asked.

"Hawaiian language?" Puna repeated, "Hawaiian's a dead language."

"ʻAʻole pololei e kuʻu moʻopuna," Tūtū called from the other room.

"E Tūtū, pehea ʻoe?" Lehia called to her with a huge grin on his face. "Hiki iaʻu ke ʻōlelo iā ʻoe?" he continued.

"ʻAe, kama, hiki nō," Tūtū replied, as she came into the kitchen. She, too, had a big smile.

"Shees," Puna said in disgust, biting into another crab leg, "speke English. Dis' America you know." He sucked hard on the soft dark shell, sucking the yellow contents into his mouth.

"ʻAʻole," Lehia replied, "this is Hawaiʻi. He Hawaiʻi au, mau a mau."

"ʻAʻoia," Tūtū replied, and they both laughed, a deep, satisfying kind of laugh.

Mōhala sat quietly on the rock, gazing out into the distant water. "E kuʻu kaikunane, ʻauhea ʻoe?" she said, addressing the water. But there was no reply, only the soft lapping of the sea at her feet. She stood up and slowly walked back to the house. By the time she got there everyone had finished eating. Everything was put away; all the dishes washed and stacked in the cupboard. Only the large green ceramic poi bowl sat in the center of the table, covered with a blue checked dish cloth. Mōhala softly opened the kitchen door and went straight to the refrigerator. She grabbed her hala lei and the pūʻolu of red fish Tūtū had prepared the day before.

"Tita girl, is that you?" Tūtū called from the other room over the blare of the television. She was watching her favorite show again, *Hawaiʻi Stars*.

"ʻAe, Tūtū, it's me. I'm getting my hoʻokupu to take down to the beach," Mōhala replied. Tūtū slowly walked into the kitchen, leaning heavily on her cane. "Oh, this arthritis; sometimes, real pilikia. Your brother had the best hands for lomilomi, make the pain go away real good." Tūtū slowly sat down in the chair nearest to where Mōhala was standing, and gently placed Mōhala's young smooth hand into her older wrinkled one. "Your brother would be proud of you, you know. Holomua. No matter what anybody say. Mai hilahila, mai makaʻu. You doin' the right thing; the ʻaumakua know that; they goin' take care of you." Mōhala leaned down and gave her grandmother a hug, and kissed the top of her forehead. "Mahalo, Tūtū," Mōhala said softly before grabbing the hala leis and pūʻolu of fish and heading out the door.

"I dunno about you, cuz," said a voice out of the shadows on the porch. "You jus' as lōlō as your braddah. Lose money dat kine stuff." Mōhala turned slowly and looked at Puna's drunken gaze. He was sitting in the creaky old rattan chair with his feet up on the railing, his ʻukulele resting on his chest. For the first time she noticed his little pot belly, the result of too many plate lunches, too many beers. She stared at him for a long, long time. Finally, she spoke, softly and deliberately.

"You know Puna, it's Hawaiians like my braddah dat try and help our people. He did his best fo' teach us how fo' respect our culture. How fo' be proud of who we are. He went back to the ʻāina and dug deep into da land, searching fo' his roots. He wen go college and look at da palapala fo' find his future. Our future, as Hawaiians. He was gonna be a great leader. He did things. Where were you at Merrie Monarch? Sitting at your girlfriend's house, drinking beer with Russell guys? Lehia was there in Hilo, chanting the story of Tūtū Pele on da stage. He was there aftah hours and hours of practice wit' Aunty Hattie's hālau."

"Yeah, but they neva win," Puna retorted.

"That's not the point Puna!" she hissed, her anger growing. "What about the protest marches? The sovereignty rallies? The Kahoʻolawe trips? Where were YOU? Where were your ʻHawaiian Blood' friends? Ho, you know," Mōhala paused, taking a deep breath, "Hawaiians like you make me shame."

"What!" Puna yelled, jumping to his feet.

"Yeah, that's right! You make me SHAME! Go, get all mad and start yelling! What you gonna do, bus' me up like all your braddah–braddah friends down the street? That's how you guys 'handle,' yeah? That, and drinking beer. Always drinking beer. You no care about where you came from, where you are, or where you going. It's Hawaiians like you –" Mōhala paused, "that wen kill my brother."

"Eh!" Puna yelled, "I neva kill nobody! I wen' love your braddah too, you know; we ʻohana."

"No," Mōhala replied, "you nevah kill him. It's your attitude, and all the braddahs like you. 'No worries, no worries,' you always told him; 'here, have a beer.' Well that's just what someone else's cousins and so-called friends did to him. 'Here, brah, have another beer.' I can just see it now. 'Have another beer and no worries. Gotta drive home? Nah, cuz, chance 'um. Ne'mind dat get adda braddahs on da road stay drinkin' too. Ne'mind get cops. No worries; have another one; yeah, one fo' da road.' So what you thought, Puna, when the phone rang at one 'o clock in the morning, and da Hilo police told my Daddy that Lehia was dead? Hit by one drunk drivah on his way home from one party. What you thought about that? Did you tell my Daddy 'no worries'? Or Tūtū? Lehia was sitting in da back of the truck an he nevah do no'ting wrong. You hear me? He nevah do no'ting wrong! And you say you nevah kill him? You might as well have!" Mōhala yelled, tears of anger, hurt and pain streaming down her cheeks.

"What's going on out here?" Aunty Aulani called, as she and Tūtū made their way onto the back porch. Mōhala and Puna were silent, glaring at each other, each with hot tears staining their flushed faces. "Well?" She demanded, looking from Mōhala, to Puna, then back to Mōhala.

"No'ting!" Puna finally said, and stalked off into the darkness. "Shit!" They could hear him say, as he made his way down to the beach, melting into the darkness.

"You okay, kama?" Tūtū asked, as she reached out for Mōhala.

"'Ae, Tūtū," Mōhala replied, sniffing back more tears. "I gotta go."

"You want company?" Aunty Aulani asked, and put her hand on Mōhala's back.

"'A'ole, Aunty, mahalo," Mōhala replied. "I think I want to be alone for a while."

"Okay Tita girl, sure thing. Hurry back." Aunty Aulani said, as Mōhala picked up her packages and headed across the yard toward the ko'a.

Aunty Aulani turned to Tūtū and sighed. "Hū, I'm glad she nevah like me go. That place gives me the creeps. I nevah go back since we wen scatter Lehia's ashes aftah the funeral. Not like I went there much before, either. Puna says since then there's a big black shark hanging out around there. Keeps saying he goin' kill 'um one of these days."

"Puna has a lot to learn," Tūtū replied with a grim look, as she turned to go back into the house.

The moon was a pale sliver in the sky, rising quickly into the starry night. "Hilo," Lehia would have told her. "The new moon is the night of Hilo." Mōhala made her way back to the ko'a, the cool sand crunching underfoot, the gentle ripples of the kai lapping at her feet. As she crossed the muliwai, she saw a glowing speck in the distance. "Damn," she thought. "I no like anybody else be here." As she approached the koʻa, Mōhala recognized the hulking shape of her father sitting on the rock. He was slouched over, his gaze fixed on the dancing water. Mōhala noticed for the first time how old he really was. "Eh Mōhala, I was wondering when you was coming," her father said warmly, crushing out his cigarette in the sand.

Mōhala said nothing as she joined her father on the rock. They sat in silence for a long time, looking at the moonlight sparkling on the ocean surface. "I didn't know you was coming," Mōhala said, more to herself than to her father.

"I couldn't come for a long time, you know," her father replied slowly.

"Yeah, I know," Mōhala replied. They relapsed into silence. A soft breeze carried the scent of līpoa to the shore, as the waves broke on the distant reef with a rumble.

"Whenevah you ready," he finally said. "It's your call. I—I don't know what fo' do," he finished, almost in a whisper.

"Don't worry Daddy," Mōhala replied, as she stood and unwrapped the pūʻolo. They stood in silence as Mōhala placed the red fish and the strands of red hala and lauaʻe lei on the smooth rock. Soon the rising tide slowly engulfed the lei, swishing it gently into the dark water. The sweet fragrance wafted up and floated into the cool night air, mixing in with the scent of salt and līpoa.

As the moon slowly rose above the clouds, Mōhala was reminded of the kupua Māui, child of the moon goddess Hina; moonchild Maui, born here on earth. Māui who tried to help his people by snaring the sun, slowing it down and increasing the daylight; by stealing the secret of fire from the ʻalae bird. Māui who fished up islands for our people to live on; Māui who died too young, trying to find the secret of immortality. "He died here in Hakipuʻu, you know" Lehia had once told her.

After a few moments Mōhala began to chant; soft and tentative. But then her voice rose like the tide itself, slowly, gently, but sure and confident, calling to the ocean, to their manō ʻaumakua, calling to the ancestors to hear their plea, to cleanse their pain, calling —

Ua hale ē, ua lele wale ē
Ua hala ē, ua lele nō
Lele i uka, lele i kai
Ua lele wale nō

Pi'i ke kai ko'o o Puna
Pi'i ka 'ehu o ke kai
E Ka'ahupahau mai ku'u ia'u
Nānā iā Lehiano'eau kau keiki
Ha'alele i ka lani
Ha'alele i ke kai
Eia ka i'a 'ula e Kamohoali'i
Eia ka 'awa no 'oe ē
Kia'i ku'u kaikunāne
E ho'omaluhia i ke kai
Ua hala 'ia o Māui i Hakipu'u
Ua hala 'ia o Lehiano'eau i Hilo
Ki'ai iā ia e Kamohoali'i
Kaikunāne o Pele, ku'u 'ohana ē
Lawe mai ia i kona wahi kau pono
I kahi pono o nā kūpuna ē.

The stillness of the air was broken only by the soft lapping of the water, and the light chatter chatter of the rustling palm leaves, whispering delicious secrets to each other. Mōhala stood in silence at the water's edge, as the cool liquid licked at her toes. Her father sat motionless in the dark, hesitant, not knowing what to do next. He cleared his throat, before speaking, the words coming slowly, "That was beautiful, Tita girl. Too bad I no can unnastan' wat you was chanting."

Without turning around, Mōhala began to recite the kanikau she had composed for her brother:

It has past, it is gone
It has passed, gone forever
Gone to the uplands, gone to the sea
It has flown...
The rough seas of Puna surge forth
The sea spray of the ocean rises
Ka'ahupahau don't forsake me
Search for your child, Lehiano'eau
Departed to the heavens
Departed to the sea
Red fish for you Kamohoali'i
'Awa for you alone

Guardian of my beloved brother
Protector in the sea
Māui died at Hakipuʻu
Lehianoʻeau died in Hilo
Guide him, protect him o Kamohoaliʻi
Brother of Pele, my family
Bring him here to his rightful place
The home of the ancestors.

Her father let out a heavy sigh. "Your braddah would be proud of you, Tita," he finally managed to say.

"I had a lot of help," Mōhala replied as she turned and went to sit with her father on the pōhaku. "I went to Lehia's Hawaiian language kumu at WCC," she said, "and he wen help me compose da chant. Did you know Hawaiians used to write chants to honor their loved ones who wen' make? They call 'um kanikau."

Her father turned to look at her, and put his arm gently around her shoulders. "No, Tita, I nevah know dat. Get plenny kine tings I nevah know dat yo' bruddah was teaching me." He sighed a heavy sigh again.

"Daddy," Mōhala asked, leaning into her father's large, warm body, "why is Puna so mad allatime? Why he like kill da shark?"

"I dunno, Tita," her father replied. "I tink Puna feels bad what happened to yo' bruddah, an' he don' know how else fo' ack. Some people get lost in their sadness; sometimes dat turn into rage. I think your cousin li'dat."

Before Mōhala could reply, a large dark mass moved swiftly through the water, causing the black water to undulate in hurried little ripples. Mōhala and her father both sat up. The large shape swam past the koʻa a ways before turning sharply and swimming back. "What—" Mōhala's father started to ask.

"The manō," Mōhala replied, in a reverent whisper.

They watched in awe as the huge dark creature rose slowly to the surface of the water, exposing its perfectly triangular fin and broad, shiny back. In one swift motion as graceful as a hula dancer, the manō grabbed the fish offering in its powerful jaws. It clutched the pūʻolo gingerly for a moment in its mouth as it swam by, like a dog with a prized toy. Mōhala and her father watched, mesmerized, as the manō slowly closed its powerful jaws around the fish, gently shaking its head from side to side. The heard a faint cracking and gurgling sound as the manō snapped its jaws closed one last time as it glided silently through the water. Mōhala couldn't be sure, but the manō seemed to be looking directly at them as it swam by, regarding them with its cool, shark gaze before turning to navigate the intricate reef passages, swimming back out to sea.

Mōhala and her father sat motionless and watched the manō swim away, too stunned to speak. Without warning, three sharp sounds pierced the air, "BANG! BANG! BANG!" The report of the rifle shots reverberated through the little valley, and echoed through the silence like thunder. It set off a round of barks and howls from the neighborhood dogs up and down the valley, and crows of alarm from the resident roosters. Mōhala and her father jumped to their feet. "What the—" her father started to say, as they heard drunken laughter coming from down the beach.

"Puna! Puna, is that you guys?" Mōhala screamed in anger, as the laughter died down to giggles. There was no answer.

"Puna!" Mōhala's father commanded, "Get ova hea!"

"'Kay Uncle," came a feeble reply. Soon a large shapeless silhouette appeared from down the beach. As it approached, it divided itself into three lanky forms, one of which held a rifle. It was Puna and his friends Russell and Wayne. In the distance, Mōhala saw the porch light come on, and Tūtū and Aunty Aulani peering into the darkness of the yard, trying to see beyond the blackness to where they stood on the beach near the ko'a.

"What da hell you guys tink you doin'?" Mōhala's father said to Puna and his friends. By the sound of his voice, Mōhala knew he was angry.

"Uh, sorry eh, Uncle," Russell responded. "We neva mean fo' make trouble. We was jus' tryin fo' nail da shahk. E'ry time we go dive, he always come boddah us." Russell hung his head a bit, waiting for Mōhala's dad's response.

"Why you guys make li'dat?" Mōhala screamed. "You don't even know what you were doing!"

"You da one who do'know wat you doin!" Puna responded, yelling back at her.

"Eh!" Mōhala's dad interrupted. "Enough. Puna, I know you guys no like da shark boddah you in da wattah, but no shoot 'um. Tūtū tol you–das kapu. No touch. You gotta show respec. Mālama da 'āina an da 'āina goin' mālama you."

"Ho Uncle," Puna said with disgust, "No tell me you believe that bull too."

"Puna," his uncle replied, "I dunno why you so hahd head. I been live a long time on dis ert, an I see planny tings. I dunno who right; the Christians say dis, the Buddhists say dat. An da Hawaiians say someting else. But I know dat if you stay angry, and you take 'um out on innocent creatures—even shahks, li'dat—dat no good. It goin' come back on you one way o' da oddah way. Which way you like um come back on you?"

Everyone was silent. Wayne and Russell shifted uncomfortably from one foot to another, the coarse sand crunching beneath their feet. Puna stared defiantly at his uncle before he spoke. "You not my faddah," Puna hissed, "An you no can tell me wat fo' do. Dat fricken shahk no belong hea. I goin' do something about it, an you no can stop me!"

"Puna–" uncle started to say, but Puna stopped him.

"No tell me wat fo do!" Puna whined. "Come on boyz, we go." Russell and Wayne stood there uncomfortably, looking first at uncle, then at Puna, then back at uncle. "Come on!" Puna commanded. They glanced at uncle with a pleading look in their eyes, and jogged away after Puna.

Mōhala turned to her father, "Why you let him talk to you like that?" she said, tears in her voice. "He has no respect for anything! Not sharks, not you—"

"Not himself," her father whispered, as he watched them disappear down the beach. "Let's go back to the house so Tūtū folks no worry." With that he turn and trudged up the beach towards the house, his footsteps heavy in the sand. Mōhala watched him for a moment and then looked back at the still water. She couldn't see anything move. Did they hit the shark? Was it injured, or worse yet—dead? She turned back and ran after her father, the sound of her feet pounding the sand like a drum, pounding in time to the beat of her heart.

Mōhala walked down the long corridor, the sound of her sandals echoing through the building. It was a cool and cloudy noontime, a typical day in the usually rainy Kāne'ohe. Outside the steep green cliffs of the Ko'olau mountains stood cloaked in clouds of gray and white. Majestic and imposing, it was a regal backdrop for the Windward Community College campus. She was looking for Kumu Keawe, Lehia's Hawaiian language teacher. Since Lehia had passed on, Mōhala had become a regular visitor to Kumu Keawe's class, and Kumu Keawe had even invited her to sit in. Mōhala was shy at first—what did she know? But with Kumu's urging, and Tūtū's encouragement, she finally decided to go.

The first few weeks she sat in the back of the class, not saying a word. Everyday Kumu had them sing Hawaiian songs, songs she recognized from family parties, songs her Tūtū occasionally got up and danced to, songs which made the other kūpuna giggle in delight, some of them even blushing.

Mōhala would go home and share what she had learned with Tūtū, Aunty Aulani, and even Daddy when he wasn't too tired from work. As usual, Puna just glared at her and said nothing. But still, she persisted.

Soon she moved closer to the front of the class, so she could see the board better. Kumu Keawe never pushed her, or made her feel shame. After a semester, Kumu asked her if she wanted to enroll at the college and take more Hawaiian language and other classes, and to her surprise, Mōhala said yes. She became busy with her classes, and didn't have time to visit the ko'a as often, but it didn't really matter—they didn't see the manō again after that night. It had vanished as quickly as it had appeared. She worried at first that Puna guys had shot the manō and killed it, but Daddy said they would have found the carcass. No, he said, it just left. It knew it wasn't wanted. Mōhala wasn't sure if she believed him, but she hoped he was right. If it wasn't dead, it might someday come back.

Besides Hawaiian language, Kumu Keawe also taught Hawaiian Studies courses. Mōhala began to sit in on those, too. One day, Kumu was lecturing about 'aumakua. Mōhala held her breath when she heard him say, "Sometimes the 'aumakua was a deified ancestor, one who was especially skilled at something. When that person passed away, their human body was gone, but their spirit was still living. Sometimes it entered another kinolau or body form like a shark, a turtle, or an owl. That's a simplified explanation, but it's the root of the 'aumakua concept." Mōhala couldn't get that idea out of her mind. She thought about it night and day; she thought about it at home and at school; she thought about it in the house and at the ko'a.

So here she was, walking down the corridor at WCC, looking for Kumu Keawe. The sound of an 'ukulele strumming, and a chorus of voices singing gaily, "Henehene kou 'aka, kou le'ale'a paha…" drifted towards her from one of the classrooms on the makai side of the building. Who else could it be but Kumu's class? She stood outside the doorway waiting until his class was pau. As he collected the songsheets scattered on his desk, Kumu Keawe glanced up and saw her standing quietly in the doorway. "E Mōhala, pehea 'oe?" Kumu asked, a bright, smile spreading across his face. "Mai, mai, come," he said, and gestured for her to enter the classroom.

Mōhala entered slowly, a bit shy. She wanted to ask her kumu a question, but didn't know where to begin. "He aha kau hana kēia lā?" he asked, seeing a mix of shyness and apprehension on her face. She didn't answer for a moment, but smiled back awkwardly. "He nīnau ka'u" she whispered, and waited for her kumu's response. "'Ae, hiki nō," he responded, "What's your question?"

"Um, remember when you was talking to the class about 'aumakua?" she asked looking down, her gaze intensely focused on her toes.

"'Ae," he said kindly, encouraging her to continue.

"Well, I was wondering…" her voice trailed off for a moment, as she looked up at her kumu. "There was one big manō that showed up in front of our hale after Lehia wen' hala. I nevah see 'um for awhile now cuz my cousin Puna dem wen shoot 'um wit' one rifle, and it nevah come back. But I left a ho'okupu and it came and took it and I was wondering…"

Kumu Keawe waited, nodding his head for Mōhala to continue.

"I was wondering," she said, "Do you think that manō is my brother?"

The room fell so silent, only the hum of the electric clock on the wall could be heard.

Kumu Keawe looked at Mōhala for a moment before replying. "Well," he started, "It's not important what I think. What do you think?"

Mōhala thought. "I not sure," she said. "I mean, seems like it could be true, 'cause of what you said in class, and 'cause of some of the things Lehia wen tell me, like the manō being our family 'aumakua. But it's hard to talk about that stuff, because nobody believes anymore."

"Oh, some people still do," Kumu Keawe replied, "but you right, not many. But just because people don't believe, does that mean it isn't true? It isn't a popularity contest; what we feel inside in our na'au can't always be explained by western science and logic. You have to look deeper than that."

"I don't know," Mōhala responded, "I guess I have to think about that more. Mahalo Kumu." Mōhala kissed him on the cheek before walking out the door. She had more questions now than ever.

The sun shone brightly in the cloudless blue sky, illuminating the brilliant blues and greens of the Ka'a'awa waters. Puna, Wayne and Russell stood on the beach at their favorite dive spot gear in hand, having one last smoke before entering the glimmering cool water. "You shooah you like go," Wayne said lazily, his voice reflecting none of the apprehension he felt, "I no like go way out an da stawm ketch aws."

"Nah, we go," Puna replied, spitting smoke out as he spoke, "Dose haole guys at da weda service, dey no know no'ting! No moa stawm. Look da sky. Dis da mos' nicest day we seen all yeah. Wat you tink Russell?"

Russell slowly sat on his haunches in a chicken fighter squat, contemplating the ocean. His black Oakleys revealed nothing; only the slight twitch of his home-made "NA KOA—BROTHERS FOREVER" tattoo on his dark and lean right shoulder revealed any hint of tension. "I do'know, brah, it's up to you guys," he said, as he took a deep drag of his cigarette and blew it out in one gigantic puff. He flicked his cigarette, still burning, at a sand crab scuttling by before standing up. "We been diving hea since small keed time; even if get one stawm, we can handle 'um. We goin be in da waddah. So what if rain—we wet awready. If get waves, we go body surf 'um in." He grinned widely, revealing two rows of perfectly white teeth which seemed to glow against his dark Polynesian skin.

"Shoots den, we go," Puna replied, with an equally dazzling smile. Puna and Russell ignored Wayne's deep scowl as they dragged their gear—fins, snorkels, masks, bags, knives, float, and spears—into the water with them. The trio made their way into waist deep water and assembled their gear, testing it out in the warm shallow water. When they were set, they slowly worked their way out along the reef into deeper waters, all the while looking out for interesting prey. Wayne tried to stay closer to shore, but Puna and Russell swam out to the edge of the reef where it joined the deep and unprotected open ocean. He thought they were crazy, and he didn't want them out there alone.

The outer edge of the reef was more dangerous, but it was also more productive; not only were there usually more fish, there were also more varieties. They had swum, dived, fished, and surfed these waters their entire lives and they weren't afraid; this part of the ocean was as familiar to them as their own back yards.

As they concentrated on their fishing expedition, they lost track of time and didn't pay much attention to the rapidly changing weather conditions above the water. Thick, heavy storm clouds rolled in quickly, stacking up against the tall Ko'olau mountains like traffic on the H-1 freeway at rush hour. And while the rising wind buffeted the surface of the water, down below they barely felt any change at all. Their diving expedition was quite successful, as each of them filled their bags with choice, succulent fish. By the time they noticed the change in the weather, they were cold, tired, and far out to sea. They were also several hundred yards south of their original dive location, and were now much nearer to Kualoa than Ka'a'awa. As Russell and Wayne surfaced, Puna waved them over to him with his hand. The choppy ocean and whipping wind, as well as the heavy bags of fish they had tied to their makeshift rubber inner tube float, made it difficult to stay afloat and hold a conversation at the same time.

"So what brah," Wayne shouted, struggling to be heard against the roaring surf and piercing wind, "You like try swim to da beach, or you like try swim to da island?" Wayne was referring to Mokoli'i, a small island off Kualoa beach park, which was just offshore from their home. "We can tell my faddah guys to drive us back latahs to get da kah."

"We go try fo da beach" Puna yelled, "Mo close to home."

"Shoots den," Wayne answered before submerging himself back into the choppy seas. Puna and Russell followed.

On a calm day, the swim from Kualoa to Mokoli'i was fairly easy; at low tide, it was even possible to wade out to the island, no swimming required. But when the weather was bad, conditions could be treacherous; not too long ago two kayakers making the short trip out to Mokoli'i from Kualoa Beach Park were caught by a sudden squall; they were lost at sea, never to be seen again. It was the power of nature that Puna guys had grown up to respect, and it was the reason that Wayne was so apprehensive to go out fishing that day in the first place.

The conditions were so bad that as they began the hazardous swim towards shore, they couldn't make any progress; it seemed that the harder they swam, the farther away the shoreline appeared, as the strong current pulled them closer and closer to Mokoli'i islet. Puna could sense the panic rising in his belly, and he struggled to stay calm. He was a strong swimmer, but being in the cold open ocean for so many hours without food, rest, or warmth was beginning to take its toll. The icy water began to anesthetize him, and he could feel his limbs going numb from overwork, and from the relentless cold. He had loosely tied the rope attached to the float around his waist, freeing his both arms so he could swim better, but the drag it created seemed to pull him back further into the foamy sea. He fumbled for his knife, and clumsily cut the rope, freeing his weakening body from the weight of his full fishing bag, where it was immediately sucked away from him in the increasingly powerful surf. Tūtū would be disappointed that he wasted it, but right now he was struggling for his own survival. Freeing himself from the drag of the float helped, but he was no match for the powerful surf which whipped him back and forth in the water like a buoy. He could feel himself slipping away, headed towards a faraway place, but he was too tired to be afraid. As he faded out of consciousness, Puna thought he heard voices chanting on the howling wind, and as his head slipped beneath the surface of the pounding waves, he felt a large rippling presence in the black water beneath him.

The steady drumming of rain falling on the tin roof was melodic, a lulling sound he had heard his entire life. As he concentrated on the soothing noise, he slowly began to make out other familiar sounds: the clinking of silverware, the soft murmur of voices—Tūtū guys talking story in the kitchen while washing dishes. Soft, easy laughter. The chirp chirp of a gecko on the window screen. He smelled 'ono smells, too, wafting into his dark bedroom:

fried fish—no; was that bacon? Mmmm. He realized he was hungry. No, ravenous. He took a deep breath, savoring the smell of freshly Cloroxed sheets that were old and smooth and soft to the touch. Warm. He never wanted to wake up from this dream. But it was too late. His foot stirred, and he heard an urgent whisper. "Puna?" It was Russell's voice. It was coming from a dark corner at the foot of Puna's bed. "Brah, you up?" Puna tried to open his eyes, but they were heavy with sleep. Why was he so sleepy? Why was Russell in his bedroom? He tried to sit up, but felt as heavy as a mountain.

A shadow fell across the doorway; Puna felt it more than saw it. "Wayne!" It was Russell's voice again. "Go tell Aunty guys Puna stay up." The shadow retreated. Puna felt the slight reverberation of the old wooden floors as his mother, Tūtū, and Mōhala came into his room. The floor trembled to the rhythm of their footsteps.

"Puna?" It was his mom. He felt the warmth of her hand caressing his forehead. "Puna, baby, are you awake?" Her voice was smooth and sure, although he heard the tinge of worry. He tried harder to open his eyes. They adjusted quickly in the dim room, and he focused first on his mother's worried face, then on Tūtū's then on Mōhala, Russell, and Wayne. "Ma," he said, slightly confused. "Wat wen happen? How come all you guys stay hea?" He looked at Russell, then at Wayne. "Eh," he said, more confused, "how come you two bozos stay wearin my clothes?" Everyone laughed. "What da hell happened?" Puna thought, a little alarmed.

"Maybe you better explain it," Aunty Aulani said, turning to Wayne and Russell.

"Ho, brah, we wen diving Ka'a'awa an was out too long an da stawm wen ketch us," Russell said.

"Yeah brah," Wayne continued. "It wen tek us da kine, almos halfway to Kailua!" he said with a smile on his face.

"Nah brah," Russell went on, "Da current wen push us almos' to Mokoli'i, but you was tired already, and you almos wen drown."

"What?" Puna replied, "An what da hell is 'Mokoli'i'?"

"Das da island, brah," Russell said, "Da kine, 'Chinaman's Hat.'"

"Why da hell you call 'um 'Moko–whatevahs'," Puna replied, "Who wen tell you dat?"

"Your cousin, brah," Russell replied, jerking his head towards Mōhala. "She smaht you know."

"Yeah," Wayne chimed in, "She know plenny kine stuffs–Hawaiian stuffs."

"No ack you guys, she no know no'ting, an you know dat," Puna retorted.

"Puna," Tūtū said sternly, "You almost wen drown out deah, and only by the blessing of Akua you still stay wit us. How you tink you wen get back hea?" Tūtū inquired, looking intensely into Puna's eyes.

"Yeah," Mōhala said. She stood at the front of his bed defiantly, arms crossed across her chest. "Why you no ask your frienz hea dat question," jerking her head back towards Russell and Wayne. Puna looked at Russell and Wayne, who looked at each other.

"You tell 'um," Wayne whispered, but Russell's face showed a look of alarm—or surprise, Puna couldn't tell which.

"Nah brah, you tell 'um," Russell whispered, as he slowly rubbed his left hand over his right shoulder where his "NA KOA—BROTHERS FOREVER" tattoo lay. Wayne just stared back at him.

"Come on boys," Tūtū said sweetly, "it's okay. Mai hopohopo. E 'ōlelo mai."

"Dat means speak up," Mōhala said, and smiled at them. They didn't know what to say.

"Okay," Russell finally said nervously. "I go tell 'um. 'Kay, Wayne was strokin' pretty good, an was almos' to da island, an I was kinda behind you when I see you go undah. I nevah tink notin' at firs, but den I never see you come right back up. I wen staht fo panic, but den I seen you come up, and I tawt dat you was okay. But den you wasn't swimming, it was like you was floating on sometin'. But you wasn't floating, cause you was moving kinda fas', an you look like you was sleeping. An den I was tryin' fo look good, an…" Russell paused, taking a deep breath.

"Go on," Tūtū whispered. "Mai hopohopo."

Russell looked at Puna wide-eyed. "Brah, I no bulai you, was one shahk was carrying you to da island."

Puna looked at everyone's faces, waiting for them to break into laughter. No one moved.

"Hahahahaha," Puna laughed. "You guys too funny. Eh, Russell, you one whatchucall, comedian, yeah? Ho, so funny." No one else was laughing. The smile left Puna's face.

"Dat's not all," Mōhala said, "dea's moah."

Russell looked at Wayne. Wayne said, "Yeah brah, I wen see 'um too. I wen get to da island, an wen I wen turn around, an deah you was, on da back of da shahk. An brah–" Wayne paused, "Dat wasn't just anykine shahk. Dat shahk had one puka in da top fin."

"Yeah brah," Russell continued, holding up his right hand, making a small circle with his thumb and his index finger, "Da puka was da size of one bullet hole."

Puna stared at them, not knowing what to say.

Mōhala sat on the large black pōhaku in front of the koʻa, watching Puna as he stood at the edge of the water. They were waiting for the moon to rise, but the night sky was already illuminated from the city lights of Kāneʻohe town across the bay, the lava-orange sodium lights reflecting sherbet colors off the swirling clouds which blanketed the tips of the Koʻolau peaks, hiding them from view. Mōhala watched as Puna bent down and picked up a few smooth coral pieces, and cast them into the sea. He whipped them out in one swift underhand motion, and the stones danced quickly a few times on the surface of the water before sinking into the shallow water.

"Akahele," Mōhala teased, "that might be Makalei, fish attracting stones. A school just might be swimming by, and they'll jump out of the ocean and into your lap."

"At least den I no need go out and spear 'um," Puna replied with a smile, and they both laughed.

Puna walked back to the pōhaku and sat next to his cousin. "So wat," he said, not unkindly, "You tink da manu–I mean, manō, goin' come?"

"I dunno," Mōhala replied, "You guys did one good job scaring 'um away."

"I —" Puna paused, hesitant to what he should say. "I sorry, cuz. I nevah mean fo' hurt 'um. I nevah know."

"I know," Mōhala replied. "But at least now you do. So what you gonna do?"

"I dunno," her cousin replied, "I still no like taro. And I no tink I can talk da kine Hawaiian. But I not goin tease you as much any moa." Puna looked at his cousin intently, rolling a piece of coral back and forth between his fingers. "I dunno if I believe dis kine stuffs. Ho, kinda spooky foah me. But you goin do 'um, az awesome. Go for it."

"I dunno what fo' t'ink sometimes, too, Puna, but I not going be scade. I gotta keep going for da 'ohana—for Lehia." Mōhala pulled her legs up onto the rock, and rested her head on her knees. "Jus' holomua," she whispered.

"Yeah," Puna replied, stretching back on the rock as if it were a recliner, "jus' holomua."

In the east the moon rose full and slowly on the horizon, sending a deep golden sheen dancing across the surface of the black sea. The dark liquid undulated slowly, breathing and murmuring in conversation with the palm trees. In the distance a dog barked lazily, and the dull hum of a television set was drowned out by the chirping of a gecko. In the aubergine depths beyond the reef a large dark shadow moved lazily in the water. Little ripples danced away from its streamlined-mass as it slowly surfaced, the pale gold light from the rising moon reflected across its broad, shiny back. A perfectly-shaped triangle fin glided smoothly through the water, marred only by a small bullet-shaped puka, through which the moonlight refracted like the eye of God.

MAKE ROPE
Imaikalani Kalahele

get this old man
he live by my house
he just make rope
every day
you see him making rope
if
he not playing his ukulele
or
picking up his moʻopuna
he making
rope

and nobody wen ask him
why?
how come?
he always making
rope

morning time . . . making rope
day time . . . making rope
night time . . . making rope
all the time . . . making rope

must get enuf rope
for make Hōkūleʻa already

most time
he no talk
too much
to nobody

he just sit there
making rope

one day
we was partying by
his house
you know
playing music
talking stink
about the other
guys them

I was just
coming out of the bushes
in back the house
and
there he was
under the mango tree
making rope
and he saw me

all shame
I look at him and said
"Aloha Papa"
he just look up
one eye
and said
"Howzit! What? Party?
Alright!"

I had to ask
"E kala mai, Papa
I can ask you one question?

"How come
every day you make rope
at the bus stop
you making rope
outside McDonald's drinking coffee
you making rope.
How come?"

he wen
look up again
you know
only the eyes move kine
putting one more
strand of coconut fiber
on to the kaula
he make one
fast twist
and said
"The Kaula of our people
is 2,000 years old
boy
some time . . . good
some time . . . bad
some time . . . strong
some time . . . sad
but most time
us guys
just like this rope

one by one
strand by strand
we become
the memory of our people
and
we still growing
so
be proud
do good

and
make rope
boy
make rope."

KUʻU WĀ LIʻI LIʻI I LĀʻIE

Olga Kalei Kalama

Papa ʻŌlelo

Kuleana - responsibility
loʻi - irrigated terrace, patch
Kalo - taro
Kōkua - help
nui - big, large
ʻohana - family

puʻu - a mound of dirt
wela - hot
loko wai - fresh water pond
ʻauwai - irrigation ditch
lūʻau - taro leaf
wai - water

Kuʻu Wā Liʻi Liʻi I Lāʻie

In a Hawaiian family, everyone had a <u>kuleana</u>, from the youngest to the eldest. Even at the tender ages of 5 and 6, my sister and I were old enough to <u>kōkua</u> with the work. One of the things we had to do was to pull weeds in the <u>loʻi kalo</u> that our ʻohana had in Lāʻie.

Every Friday evening we would travel the old Pali road, through Kāneʻohe along the Koʻolau coastline to Lāʻie. We would always arrive at dark, so the work began early Saturday morning. I can just hear my grandmother saying over and over "Ala, ala". This means "wake up", yet it was still dark outside. We always rose early to get a headstart on the sun.

The work on Saturday varied from time to time, depending on the need. There was preparation of new <u>loʻi</u>, tilling the soil, planting, harvesting, and weeding. There were always weeds to be pulled. Weeds! Weeds! Weeds! There was no end. Sometimes the weeds were so <u>nui</u> that we couldn't pull them up. Grandma said to step on it, loosen the hold of the roots, then pull it up - it worked!

After pulling the weeds, we would roll it into a ball and stuck it back into the mud near the <u>puʻu</u>. My question was, "why?" Grandma said it was like fertilizer. Besides, it was not for us to question our elders, just do as we were told. Grandma was always spouting words of wisdom that we remember and make use every day of our lives.

Needless to say, pulling weeds can be very tedious, especially when the sun is <u>wela</u>. We were always trying to find ways to "cool off."

Since the <u>kalo</u> grew 2 to 3 feet tall and had large, umbrella-like leaves, we would sit in the mud and hide under the <u>lūʻau nui</u>. The mud was cool and felt good between our toes. However, the weeds were still there and we had to keep working. Ever so often we would her grandma's voice calling to us to see where we were and much work we had done.

One hot Saturday, we decided to go swimming in the <u>loko wai</u> that supplied water for irrigation of all the <u>loʻi</u>. But grandma was working in the lo'i between us and the lokowai. How were we going to get to the lokowai without being seen? Surely she would see us and we might be punished. We weren't allowed to play until the work was done.

A long, narrow 'auwai ran along the far bank, carrying water to the lo'i from the lokowai. The 'auwai was about 2 or 3 feet wide, the banks were about 3 feet high in most places, and wai was about 1½ to 2 feet deep. To a 5 and 6 year old, this 'auwai was perfect

We crawled in the mud, hidden by the lūʻau nui, and made our way to the bank of the 'auwai. Then, we peeked over the top of the lūʻau to see where Grandma was working. When she bent over to do some work, we quickly climbed over the bank and slipped into the cool, clear, clean water of the 'auwai. We swam upstream as quietly as possible until we reached the lokowai.

The lokowai was surrounded by a cement wall with a water trough on one side. If you block the trough with plywood, the water in the cement tank fills up to about 6 feet high. Excellent for swimming. We swam quietly and enjoyed the cool, clean water. It was refreshing and lots of fun. We were quiet so Grandma wouldn't know where we were.

Soon we heard her voice calling. Playtime was over and we had to return to work. We returned to the lo'i by the same way that we left - downstream in the 'auwai, over the bank into the lo'i, and wiggle through the mud to our weeding spot. When she called again, we stood up out of the mud and answered her.

When she saw us, she said, "You two are still in the same place. Get busy and finish your work. If you don't finish, you can't go swimming." My sister and I looked at each other and smiled.

As we remember these childhood memories, we wonder if Grandma knew what we were doing. Did she know that we were swimming instead of working? We never knew for sure and she never told us one way or the other. I think she did know. What do you think? -- By olga kalei kalame

My kupuna wahine was a very special person. She was a strong woman physically, mentally and spiritually. I remember her with fondness and love. She made many sacrifices and shed many tears because of me, and I am grateful. I think of her everyday of my life and appreciate all that she did for me. Her teachings and love have helped to give my life some direction and meaning. Many things I do today are the result of her goodness. I continue to grow, learn, share, and enjoy life because of her. Many people have touched my life but no one has had a greater influence than she. I love her and miss her. Thank you for letting me share. (kalei)

LEI MAKER

Lisa Linn Kanae

She sits like an ipu balanced on the lauhala floor. Her ankles crossed, knees jut out beneath her vermillion mu'u mu'u. She spears the stiffened tip of floss, clean and quick, through to the opposite side of a stainless-steel eye, then pulls   pulls out a long piece of floss. She dips her fingers into a pile of papery orange. Selects one pua. She pierces its center, then tenderly   tenderly draws it along the length of floss. Pick pierce gently pull then pick, she looks up at the customers, gently pull then pick then pierce. Will they buy or just look, gently pull then pick, they, who come from office spaces, Acuras and airplanes. Will they take one look then go next door? Pick four pua pierce all one time. There's the lease, gently pull, and the license, gently pull, and general excise tax, gently pull, and the heat. Tour buses, city buses, mopeds, cars. Silver mylar balloons bump bump bump against the fluorescence light fixture. Glass refrigerator doors weep condensation. Pick pierce pull. Pick pierce pull, gently pull, then knot the ends. She lays her lei along side the others, rows and rows of Royal Ilima waiting to be bought on the lauhala floor.

MAKE MANU: MANU MAKE

(dead bird: death bird)

Lino Kaona

My old Grandfather,
    Bearded, long haired,
Burned very dark by the sun,
    Kupuna Kāne: Naʻauao Makua   *(clever old fellow: wisdom's father)*
Lived in the old style
    In a one-room-house he built
Near Hālawa on Molokaʻi.

Māʻalo ke kai ea.   *(giant wave passing)*

When I was a boy
    He taught me
To see the stars as they are
    And to place my hands dry
Upon the oily smooth surface of the sea.
    Māʻalo ke kai emi: Ka pau ʻana!   *(giant energies pass: ending comes!)*

The hot bright day
    When the net of the world's form
Was stretched to bursting
    Across the truth of things,
Containing it as best it could,
    A silver airplane flew by,
Passing Kikipua Point,
    Looking for Hoʻolehua Field.

My grandfather's face changed
    Like clouds before the sun,
His whisper was like echo-wind:

Lele ka ʻiwa   (*frigate-bird*
I ka nani   *flies in beauty*
Hōʻeleʻele ka mikini mokulele   *machines*
I ka lani.   *darken the sky.*)

My grandfather stood waist-deep
    In the sea
Until after sunset,
    When the wind returned,
But his eyes were tightly closed.

LOVE IS ALL WE NEED
Temujene Hanae Makua

> *Little darling, don't you cry no more . . .*
> *Love is all we need*
>
> *— Ulise*

I'm in bed looking at the ceiling and the reflection of headlights as a car zooms by. I have seen this on every ceiling in every bed I've ever slept in. On nights when I can't fall asleep, instead of counting sheep I count headlights. I have had many restless nights of counting headlights, nights when I have no clue where my mind will take me. But I guess I've gotten used to it. No one can see me or hear me, and that way they can't ask what's wrong. I've been doing this since I was four. And by that time in my life I had experienced things many other four-year-olds had not.

> *We've got to struggle for what the world*
> *be searching for . . .*

They met at work, and even from the beginning, they had problems. Problems that both of them saw coming, but neither could have avoided or prepared for. My mother had an overly self-conscious personality with festering insecurities about needing to be loved. Her first marriage had ended in a shameful divorce where a few family members said, "I told you so."

My father had a commitment problem. Monogamy was not a word he understood. And he drank too much.

It started with my father not coming home every day and having too many unaccountable hours. This made my mother so paranoid that she'd stay up all night calling everyone she knew. When he finally walked into the house, sometimes just minutes before she'd leave to go to work, she'd pounce on him, "Where the hell were you? What were you doing?" On nights when my father did come home he was so hung over that he would be late to work the next morning because he passed out in the shower. A couple of times my mother received a call in the middle of the night to come down to the police station and bail out my dad because he had been picked up for DUI.

Years later, my mother would tell me stories about the crazy things she and my father did. How one time when I was only an infant she got so pissed at my dad that she grabbed me and jumped in the car. Flying down

H-1 at 90 miles per hour, my father caught up with her and rear-ended her a few times until she pulled over. She told me once that she and Dad got into an argument over the phone and she hung up on him. When she returned home my father had taken a bat to every wall and piece of furniture in the house, including the waterbed and her dresser. The long nights and early mornings were a part of everyday life, along with the endless fights and beatings they dished out. These fights receded only when the neighbors called the police.

And this was it: the downward spiral that inevitably led to the separation of our family. To me, it all happened so fast that before I knew it the house was mortgaged, the cars repossessed, the bank accounts drained, and I was spending Christmas at my auntie's. When Auntie could no longer take care of me because she had four children of her own, I moved away.

Love will ease the pain, wipe the tears away . . .

My youngest sister Uluwehi and I lived with a woman in Waikāne. I don't think we ever knew her name or where exactly in Waikāne she lived. She just told us to call her "Grandma." Every morning when we woke up we were only allowed to stay in the house for fifteen minutes, just enough time to brush our teeth and change our clothes. Once our fifteen minutes were up we had to go outside. Grandma was so afraid that our red-dirt feet would get her white carpet and plastic-covered furniture dirty that we even had to use the outside toilet and basin when we bathed.

She had five other children whom we hated and constantly fought with for food. This was the first foster home we lived in. For three years we moved around nomadically, addressing these strangers as "auntie" and "uncle" like they were part of our family. Uluwehi and I always stayed together as we moved, helping each other to readjust to our new home.

Heaven help us, help us find our way . . .

Christmas was always a difficult time. Christmas 1988, we visited our mother in the hospital. She had attempted suicide by drinking poison and slitting her wrists. As we climbed into bed with her she told us to be careful about the little tubes coming from her neck, heart, and nose. We played with her mechanical bed, adjusting the feet and head positions, thinking that this was the coolest thing we had seen and each wanting one for Christmas. For Christmas that year, she gave us a stuffed butterfly. When you squeezed tightly the face lit up and smiled at you.

Every Sunday was our visiting day with Dad. We'd do things like go to the rec center or Ice Palace. These were always fun times. In the evening we attended AA meetings with him. All the adults would sit in a big circle with their chairs facing each other. They would talk and sometimes cry, but I never had the curiosity to listen so I went out and played with the other children. At the end of each session everyone joined hands in prayer. The meeting would conclude with a chorus of voices chanting, "Keep coming back. It works."

Maybe someday, maybe we'll find our way . . .

And it did work. Everything worked out.

It was some time when I was in first grade that Uluwehi and I had to readjust for the final time. We reunited as a family after three years of separation, and moved into a little apartment in Kalihi. These times were challenging. There were snapshot moments when I saw my father reenacting his old ways, moments when I thought he would relapse. When these moments occurred, the very next day we would all attend an AA meeting to support him. We kept going to these meetings until we were sure Dad was fully recovered. And even then, every once in a while, we'd attend a meeting just for the heck of it. My mother continued to seek psychiatric counseling until she too was fully healed.

Love is all we need to keep happiness in our family . . .

Today I look at my family and we continue to struggle. My mother slips in and out of employment, every month my father stresses over paying bills, and about seven months ago, we received a devastating blow that Uluwehi was pregnant. She's due two weeks after my graduation.

"Never a dull moment," someone once told me. I see nothing in my parents that reminds me of our ugly past. But sometimes when I'm sitting on the bus I'll see an advertisement for domestic violence or I'll be watching TV and a commercial for alcoholism comes on. And for an instant, just a heartbeat, I am reminded of the past, of where we have come from to where we are today. I am convinced that our past is not ugly, but victorious and triumphant, and that everything I am today, a fighter, a survivor, has derived from our victory. My family's unrelenting spirit has made me.

THEY CALLED HIM MANGO MAN

Jasmine Tua

His feet were engraved with years of abuse; the skin on them had long since become like the bark of a tree that has seen many seasons. They were cracked and chiseled; dry and worn down. The arch of his foot was long past gone; his flat feet had now formed a permanent sole from the many layers of calluses. His toenails were grotesquely decorated with mud. The crevices between finger and nails were outlined with embedded particles of earth.

The unusual sight of his skin could only be surpassed by the matted rug of a hair-do that he sported. I could not help but wonder how many years of neglect it had taken to cause the strands of hair and collective filth to become a single entity.

His body was frail and thin, reminiscent of a twig of straw ready to snap in a stiff wind. As I watched him, I realized he lacked equilibrium. He staggered along on the side of the road in Kailua town, arguing vehemently with himself about who knows what, twitching his body left and right as he walked. He looked to me to be about sixty years old, but was probably only thirty. His face was narrow and long. His expression never changed. His tired eyes and drawn mouth spoke volumes of sadness.

I remember the first time I saw him. We were slowly cruising by the video store. I glanced out the window of the car and saw what looked like a dirty old man wearing a blanket on his head. I yelped out to my mother, "Mom, look! He looks so weird."

My mother looked at the ragged man and said, "Stop staring; he's not bothering you."

I felt ashamed.

My next encounter with the Mango Man involved one of my best friends, Kalena. We had just gulped down a Slurpee from 7-Eleven and the brain freeze was coming. As we dallied along the side of a busy intersection, there perched Mango Man under a banyan tree, staring into space. We cautiously crept around him, but something forced me to say, "Howzit brah."

He took a nasty, fierce look at me as if he were ready to snap, then he turned around and mumbled something like, "What! You damn kid." I was not offended just shaken by his harsh glance.

"What the heck did you think you were doing? Why did you say hello, he could have killed us!" my friend Kalena said, in a state of shock.

"I don't know. I felt like being friendly," I replied.

"He is so weird, my mom said to stay far away from him."

I guess I was feeling sorry for him because I replied, "Why? He is just a poor old man in rags, going a little crazy."

"Did you see the way he looked at us, ready to pounce or something," said my friend.

"Ah, aren't you just overreacting a little? Why do they call him Mango Man anyway? He doesn't look like a mango," I questioned.

"Well, from what I heard, he goes in people's yards and snatches all the good mangoes off the trees. Then he picks up the rotten ones and throws them at houses or at people just for fun."

I could not believe Kalena actually was that naive and believed that.

"And you believe that?" I asked.

"Why not? He looks so weird."

"He's probably just an old man with no money, that doesn't really do anything to anyone, and just because he looks like that, people say he does all those bad things."

I thought to myself, where did he come from before time and circumstances transformed him into "The Mango Man"?

Maybe he has had a terrible life. I'm sure it must not have always been like this for him. Was he ever happy, living in a nice, safe home with lots of loving family members and plenty of food? Does he have any pleasant memories to draw on when he becomes lonely in his isolated existence? Maybe this is his choice because the world has become too unbearable for him and he has, in his own way, removed himself from our everyday problems and stress. He may be happy in his detachment from society; maybe he likes eating mangoes. It's possible that he may think plump mangoes are gold, yet to us they are just an everyday local fruit that costs pennies. He may be tired of the same old fruit. Has he proudly tried pickling, drying and whatever else it takes for the plain, familiar taste to disappear? Or maybe he is satisfied with his simple style of living. He made me think how I take those simple pleasures for granted and how not everyone is as fortunate as me.

KULĀIWI

BEARING THE LIGHT

N. Keonaona Aea

Everywhere—black. The ocean and sand are without color except for where we stand. We move forward, water lapping at our knees and rolling over exposed rock. I glance up. Ahh, more light—real light, a million white eyes that never blink. Even at day. For whatever I am doing here, I ask mercy of the night.

Glenn raises a hand and whispers, "Come closer, Babe. I think I see something. 'Kay holdit. That's good."

I sway back and forth, hoping the wana and sharp coral won't cut through the tattered soles of my Nikes. I wiggle my toes, I wiggle my heels. Sand. I stare at my bare legs and arms. Goosebumps.

"Hold still," Glenn says. He raises his spear and plunges it downward like Thor throwing a lightning bolt.

I feel—rather than hear—a crunch near my foot. I take two shaky steps back, wave the net and snarl, "You almost hit my foot, you just missed it by—"

"Awright!" Glenn cries. He laughs as he stares past the widening ripples. "I got it! Wooooooo, tako and poi tomorrow. Tako and poi!" He lifts the spear then frowns at the brown lump impaled on it.

"What *is* that stuff, Glenn? Man, it's oozing blood."

"Watchit," my boyfriend says. He points to my hands. "Don't drop it. don't get it wet."

"I know, I know." I raise the lantern past my head and our shadows lengthen.

Glenn slides the shriveled thing from his spear. "Sea cucumber," he mutters, tossing it past the circle of light. "C'mon, let's go further out."

I'd rather go further in. Like back to the dry Subaru, back to my warm apartment, back to a hot shower. Back in a place with lamps, and a stereo, and a pair of sweat pants. Instead, I walk beside Glenn and try not to bang my knees against the rocks.

My hair was already curled, and I was ironing a dress when Glenn phoned earlier this evening. He was supposed to take me to Spats, but he said that according to his tide calendar (Damn, I thought, I *knew* I shouldn't have given it to him for Christmas)—according to the calendar, tonight was a good night for torchfishing and would I mind if we did that instead of going to Spats. "We'll celebrate your birthday tomorrow," he said.

More than anything I wanted to say, "No way, Glenn. I ain't into sloshing after morays." But he was saying something about "perfect conditions," and how all I'd do was hold the light and maybe a net, and how I'd get the hang of it because it wasn't that hard. That's what he said.

Well, whatever this Coleman burns, it's giving me a headache. And my eyes hurt, and what's these pointy things that keep jabbing my legs? We've probably been here for at least an hour. Maybe if we head back to shore now we can make it to Spats. "Glenn? Hey Glenn—what time izzit?"

He straightens from a hunched position and squints. "What? What were you saying?"

I tap my wrist. "Time."

He glances at his watch. "Little after nine. We been here almost twenty minutes. Let's go further out and walk parallel to shore. There's more people coming."

About a hundred yards to the left, a light seems to be approaching. Three people (including a child) are clustered around it. Sounds like they're laughing, or singing, or telling jokes. ("Knock knock." "Who's there?" . . .) Maybe they're a family. Or neighbors, or casual acquaintances. Maybe it doesn't matter. Some things don't when you're having fun. Whatever that is.

The shore is . . . it is . . . I glance left, right, left . . . the shore is . . . there. That must be it where the irregular string of lights are. Doesn't Glenn realize how far we've walked? (Walked? Ha! More like stumbled.) I'm not accustomed to sinking from knee-high to chest-deep water within a matter of one or two steps. Tricky, tricky, the depth of these holes. Six inches equals one foot.

Fluorescent shrimp eyes, pairs of orange beads staring from holes I'd rather not poke. Kind of reminds me of Christmas, those eyes.

God, the stillness!

Could this really be the same beach where sunbathers and families congregate during the day? What happens to the jabber when the sun sets? Where are the swaggering hard-bodies, the confident lifeguards, and intense frisbee-flingers?

This cubic night and acres of silent, ancient ocean has metamorphosized us. Glenn and I, tentative intruders. The flip side of haughtiness—humility.

I carry the lantern in the crook of my arm, hugging it to my body. Friendly heat, warm eye. I think of the empty plastic bag in Glenn's backpack. He wants to catch an eel, some weke, trumpet fish, tako, *anything*—he says. As long as it's something.

Earlier, he paused in mid-step, lowered his face to the water. "Bring the light real close," he whispered. "I think it's an eel. Looks like some kind of dark eel against the sand there."

He plunged the spear forward (THOOMP) and his eyes widened. Happy green eyes. "It hardly moved. I got it, I got it!"

"Ha!" I said when he lifted his catch. "Some eel. From the Schwinn family, I suppose."

He pulled the inner tube off the prongs and shrugged. "Can't see everything clearly without perfect light."

We stumble on. I learn to dig the toe of my shoes into small holes, press my foot over the contours of the rocks. I slip once or twice landing on my okole without dunking the lantern. "Good job," Glenn says. "You're getting the hang of it."

I ask him about the silvery-blue fish that keep poking my legs, and what're these things skimming over the water. "Needle fish," Glenn says. "They're okay. Won't gore through your legs."

He swishes the net back and forth, back and forth. Sometimes he scoops up rocks, bottles, palm fronds, part of a hibachi. But sometimes the net lives: baby Weke, Tang, Spanish Dancer, Puffer, Moorish Idol, and now, a spotted Cowfish that sits in my palms. It is smooth, hard and boxy. I hold it against my ear and stare at Glenn. Sounds like it's crying, I say. It's making these high beeps.

He takes the fish and strokes its sides, taps the horn, pretends to kiss its lips. "These make neat pets," he says. "If I had a fish tank, I'd keep one."

We talk about nothing, about everything. He tells me he can see through the white shorts and that the needle fish left small red dots on my thighs. He says I look better without eye shadow, and my hair looks nice when it's curled, and why did I wear opal earrings to go torchfishing? He slaps the water. "God," he says. "I never saw such perfect conditions as tonight!"

But you didn't catch anything, Glenn. Except a sea cucumber and the inner tube from some kid's bike.

He nudges me lightly with his spear and says, "I just caught a two-ton whale. A whale in short shorts."

"It's about eleven," Glenn says. "Let's go. tide's coming in." I'm tempted to ask him to put out the light. I want to know what it's like to be a complete foreigner in this element I know well. I *thought* I knew well. Tonight was different—not fun—but different. Kind of like walking into church during mid-prayer.

Glenn puts an arm around my waist and says, "Tomorrow we'll stay as long as you want at Spats."

I nod absentmindedly. There must be at least five pounds of sand in each shoe . . . and boy, that was a cute Cowfish . . . and the way that lantern hovers over the water out there makes me think of the times we'd go camping and we'd be the only light on the mountain for miles.

Maybe Glenn'll buy me some rubber tabis for my birthday. Either that, or a wetsuit and my own net.

PRESS DOWN

Keith Kalani Akana

Press down into the earth
Turn your foot at a slight angle and press down
Alternate your feet in pressing
Press down, exert pressure!
Through every sinew and fiber of your thigh
Through and using the force of your calves
Press down!

Now, take root as you become part of
The rhythm of life
Let your back become as straight as the trunk of a koa
Let your arms brandish in the wind like the branches of a tree
Let your mind bear fruit, ripe juicy mountain apples
And let brilliant lehua blossoms spring forth from your temples
Forming a lei around your head.

Press down to the right.
Press down to the left.
Make sure that your toes, even your littlest toe,
Dig deep into the soil.
Let the padding of your foot feel it
Let the heel of your foot feel it
It is good, is it not?
To have each blade of grass absorbed
And every particle of dirt or sand now ingrained
That you are indistinguishable now
From the firmly rooted coconut tree
So sway why don't you?
Abandon yourself to the wind
Whose origin is the same as yours
Take root and blossom forth
In native soil
Whose origin is the same as yours
Plant yourself firmly
In the universe
Whose origin is the same as yours.
Your origin thus says
Press down!

SPEAR FISHER

Joseph P. Balaz

In Kona
a Midwest businessman
    caught a marlin,
and hung it upside down
      on a wharf —

    At Hale'iwa
    I caught a kūmū,

      and I ate it.

Off Pōka'i Bay
an Australian competitor
    caught a tuna,
and hung it upside down
      on a wharf —

    At Kawailoa
    I caught an 'āweoweo,

      and I ate it.

Near Makapu'u
a "Jaws" adventurer
    caught a shark,
and hung it upside down
      on a wharf —

    At Pūpūkea
    I caught an āholehole,

      and I ate it.

In the Honolulu press
and the tournament boxscore,
egos reap the ocean of trophies —

On the North Shore of O'ahu,
I harvest a gift of life.

OLD MAN PUEO
Keola Beamer

Lord I've seen some pretty sights and I haven't seen them all I've been told
I've never seen a prettier sight than I have on the South Point Road
Old Man Pueo, he was standin' on a stone, his body framed by sunset and
the sea
Old Man Pueo, he's always so alone, his feathers caught the colors in the sky
O Heavenly Father please, o Iesu please, I'd give everything that I need, if
some day my life could be so free.
I nā pali o ka 'āina, i nā ua kuahiwi, ola mau loa, ola mau loa, he inoa no ka mana o
ka pueo

Lord I've spent some sleepless nights and my heart has been confused I
know
My Life has been a bumpy road and I wish that it could have flowed
Old Man Pueo could I borrow the strength in your wings? Would they lift me
from the darkness to the sun?
Old Man Pueo I'm a stranger in your sky, and I think that you have helped
me in your own way. O Heavenly Father please, o Iesu please, I'd give every
thing that I need, if some day my life could be so free.
I nā pali o ka 'āina, i nā ua kuahiwi, ola mau loa, ola mau loa, he inoa no ka mana o
ka pueo

FISHPOND
Marjorie Edel

The official document says "it was a pond
and its integrity is still there.
It's a very ancient place."
We try to make it right
for the people who are dead
for the people who are alive
longing for an ancient place —
and of course for the fish.

The fish are what they are
as they always have been feeding on the weeds
and the food stirred on the pond's bottom
by turtles as they make their way
nibbling their own weed. At midday
the fish find a place under ledges and plants
a shelter from radiation which stabs shallow water.
Ponds find their place along the lava coast
sheltered by bays and grow
their flora and fauna. When man came
finally to the islands he protected ponds
for his own use. Other men came
were careless, destroyed.

The mullet goes on being mullet in the old way
not knowing the pond is an ancient place
or having use for integrity.

KA MO'OLELO O KE ALANUI

Dana Naone Hall

More than four hundred years ago,
as it comes down to us,
the road was built by Kihaapi'ilani,
who spread his cape over Maui.
When the 'ōhi'a blossoms were
tossed by the wind
he travelled to the island of Hawai'i
to ask for 'Umi's help,
and returned with a fleet of canoes
and warriors to conquer Hāna.
From Hāna the rest of the island
fell to him like a ripe fruit.
In the years that followed,
the farmers and fishermen,
native tenants of the land,
placed on the brow of the coast,
as it circled the island,
a road to catch the falling sound
of the runner's feet.
Kūkini carried messages past
petals of cliffs opening in mist.
Near the shore, the akule,
silver black and still quivering,
was divided among
the paddlers and those who helped
bring in the nets.
The white tapa hung from the pole
announced the arrival of Lono Makua
during the Makahiki.
Feathers and the food of the land
were brought to the ahu
along the road where the god
in his pig form was waiting.

Closer to our time, cattle
crossed the road and were herded
to the anchored boat.
Poi, wrapped in ti leaves,
came by way of another boat from Kīhei.
Horses, oxen and wagons stirred up
the dust on the road,
pausing at the one store, where hands
exchanged things over counters,
then continued on into this century.

Now there is car surf on the road
and the waves keep breaking.
Dust mixing with salt air.
After all these years,
we are being told that the road
will be closed. Those who propose it
don't know that the road is alive.
Give up the road they tell us
and it will be replaced
with a sign that says
we can get to the beach this way,
only don't get off the path
or cut across the grass,
and hang on to your children
not to mention don't let go of your
cooler until you hit the sand.
For all your troubles
there'll be a comfort station
in the parking lot (a comfort to whom?)
and even a concrete trail
to mark where the old road once passed
between the hotel and the beach,
open so many hours a day
and closed when the sun goes down.

The lizard woman is talking
but who is listening?
At night,
when the island is deep
     in the crater of sleep,
across the channel
   the moʻo
     raises its head
one eye reflecting the moon.

WAIMAKA

Hina Kahanu

> *Jim Lomax was my ipo for 17 years. When he died,*
> *my hoaloha, Makia Malo, gave me hospitality at Kalaupapa.*
> *The bright waters of Kalaupapa helped me heal.*

Above Makia's cottage
I see two silver and white
waterfalls running down the face
of the pali.
I tell Kalaupapa, I love and miss Kimo.
And Kalaupapa, of course, understands.
So many graves here,
so many confessions of grief.
Mauka and makai,
her waters glisten back.

A SHARK ATTACKS
George Kahumoku, Jr.

On a warm, sunny Sunday a couple of days before Christmas, I was out in the sea in an outrigger canoe a mile off the coast of Kona, on the Big Island of Hawai'i. Just a few months before, I was flying high over this same ocean at 600 miles per hour returning from several years of college on the mainland.

During those years, I had felt so separated from my home and culture. But on this day, I would be living the life my ancestors had lived for generation after generation, fishing in the waters around the island. The softly perfumed breeze of the trade winds, and the ocean swells lapping quietly against the boat felt comfortable and familiar. And yet, after years in a big mainland city, it was kind of an adventure, too.

This adventure actually began the day before. I was wrapping up class at the school where I taught. The classroom, on the side of a volcano and surrounded by palm and guava trees, was decorated with the usual Christmas stuff — pictures of sleighs, cardboard snowmen, paper icicles and snowflakes cut out of folded paper. I hoped Santa wouldn't be expecting chimneys here, or we'd be in big trouble.

Late in the day, I saw my 15-year old nephew, Sweetie, hanging around just outside the classroom. He was acting so nervous and sneaky, you couldn't help but notice him. Finally the bell rang, but he waited for the classroom to empty before he came in. It wasn't like Sweetie to be anywhere near school when he didn't have class, and I wondered what was up.

"Aloha, Uncle."

"Eh, Sweetie, howzit?"

He made one final check around the room to make sure we had privacy. "You still got some 'ōpelu?"

The 'ōpelu is a type of mackerel, very tasty. A few weeks before, we'd had a good run on them. I'd saved a few dozen frozen in seawater in milk cartons. Sometimes during the winter months, when 'ōpelu was scarce, it was handy to have some available for bait. Sweetie was about the only person who knew I had them.

"Yeah, still got some. Why?"

Sweetie took a long, careful look over each shoulder before stepping closer and confiding, "Ahi."

The magic word. When the ahi, the yellowfin tuna, were running, you had a chance to make some real money. I hadn't been paying attention to prices lately, but Sweetie, like me, came from a long line of fishermen and he stayed on top of stuff like this.

"How much they going for?" I whispered. Now I was part of this conspiracy.

Sweetie checked the room again before showing me three extended fingers. He grinned at my surprised reaction. I began to slip from the "textbook" English of a school teacher into my native pidgin.

"Holy shit!" I said. "Tree bucks one pound?"

"Mitchy Alani wen catch one 80 poundah yestahday."

"How you know dis?"

"Arley seen it. He wen see Mitchy bring da canoe in." Arley was Sweetie's little brother. He was only nine years old, but a *very* reliable source of information.

"Somebody else wen see'em?"

"Nah. Jus da same guys down dere. Mitchy said he nevah catch nutting. But Arley tink he acting kinda funny kine, so da buggah stick aroun' when everybody wen go. He wen go climb da coconut tree and go hide on top da tree. Mitchy wen go back to da canoe. He wen take one ahi, put da buggah inside his truck and take off. Arley seen da whole ting."

You don't put anything over on Arley. So the ahi were running, and I had the bait.

"Sweetie, you got some hooks, brah?"

"No, brah."

This was a problem. I knew I had two, maybe three hooks. Hell, if we started buying or worse, borrowing these huge #11 ahi hooks, word would be all over Kealia in hours. Then we'd have 50 other canoes out there trying to catch ahi. It may be the "Big" Island, but it's a small world here when it comes to stories about an ahi run. Sweetie and I decided we'd have to go with whatever we had. We agreed to meet early the next morning at the beach. I'd supply the bait and tackle and outboard motor, and Sweetie would arrange for a canoe.

Just before dawn the next morning, Sweetie and I were driving in my ancient Jeep Wagoneer along the road to a beach near Kealia. We were looking for Arley. Arley was out looking for rocks. He seemed to have gotten lost. I hated driving around like this because my clutch was slipping pretty bad. Parts are expensive in the islands and I was putting off repairs until I had a few extra bucks.

Finally, my headlights picked him up walking along the edge of the road, a skinny kid in well-worn swim shorts, no shirt, no shoes. He was carrying an old white plastic spackle bucket. I saw him bend over to pick up a rock, look it over carefully, and toss it away. No wonder it was taking him so long to collect a bucket of rocks. I pulled the truck up next to him.

"Eh! What you get?" I said, and opened the door for him. He held up the bucket for me to see what was inside, three dozen or so baseball-sized rocks.

"Yeah, dat's 'nuff," I told him. He put the bucket in the back of the truck and climbed in. I put the jeep in gear with a grinding crunch and we headed down to the beach.

"Eh Arley. Dah ahi going fo' three bucks a pound, yeah? So how much fo' one fish weigh 80 pounds?" A question from Mr. Kahumoku, high school teacher. Arley worked the problem in his head, then looked at me in astonishment.

"Dat's 240 bucks!"

Smart kid.

"Fo' one fish?" he asked.

"Fo' one fish."

"Shit! Drive fastah, Uncle."

I laughed, "Gotta catch 'em first." Kids think it's so simple. But it was a chance to pick up, on my one day off, maybe a couple of months' teachers' salary for me, and a year's pay for Sweetie.

We drove on down to the beach, where the canoe was supposed to be. Sweetie's dad, Uncle Poli, was always bragging about his wonderful canoe. But a couple of people had told me to look for a canoe with the ugliest paintjob ever seen on a boat of any size. I laughed at the time, but it was no damn joke. This thing was painted a bright, horrible orange color. It wouldn't have been so bad if the paint hadn't had some kind of ugly fluorescence to it. Poli had painted it a year ago using some marine paint he got on a closeout at Sears. No wonder he got it cheap. The *ama*, the outrigger, was all waterlogged and busted up. It was held together with baling wire, old hand line and enough duct tape to keep the Titanic floating.

"Dat's it," Sweetie said.

"What kine canoe dis? Hooo, dat one ugly buggah!" I said. He couldn't really disagree. It kind of took your breath away. We shut down the truck and got out and walked over to the thing.

"You sure da buggah not goin' sink?" I said.

"Nah, Pops says she no leak."

Some people might think it's kind of risky going after large gamefish in deep water with hand lines in a 24 foot boat, even when the equipment is in top condition. With this canoe beneath us, we would really be letting it all hang out.

But the sun was coming up and there wasn't much choice at this point, so the three of us loaded our gear into the canoe and launched it into the surf. Arley would be staying behind. His job was to get a couple of our cousins to meet us when we came back in.

About an hour later, we were maybe half a mile offshore, propelled by my Dad's old 25 horse Evinrude outboard. The sea was calm and the blue-green water was crystal clear. The canoe sat low in the water, weighted down with ice coolers, bait box, a couple of pails of rocks plus two large guys and an outboard engine.

Sweetie and I got busy setting up our fish tackle. First I grabbed one of our 'ōpelu baitfish and put it on the blade of my paddle, which I had laid across the gunwales to use as a cutting board. I cut the 'ōpelu in half, slitting the fish right up the middle. One half, I cut into pieces. I picked up a rock from a bucket and used the other half of the 'ōpelu to wrap up both the rock and the cut-up pieces of fish. I embedded the huge three inch ahi hook tied to the end of my line into the large piece of 'ōpelu. I tied a slip knot with the line around the whole thing. Sweetie rigged his up the same way. We had done this often before, and it was fast and easy work for us.

I picked up the 400 pound test hand line. It's made up of several lines woven together, with small lengths of string we stuck through it every six feet, each string marking a fathom. We measured this by stretching out a length of the line overhead, with our arms widespread. That's a fathom. We'd be fishing down between one hundred and two hundred feet.

"No foget, we only got tree hooks, you know, so no spoil 'em eh," I reminded Sweetie. "Tree should be 'nuff if we jus play 'em nice and easy."

I picked up my tackle and dropped it carefully over the side, then started feeding out line with my hands. Sweetie gathered his up and did the same. We could see the tackle descending deeper and deeper into the crystal clear water for a long, long time. We watched it go down until it disappeared from view in the deep.

The rock is a weight. The ahi is a deepwater fish. You need to get down at least 40 fathoms to where he lives. When you get the bait down to where the ahi are, you give your line a jerk. The slip knot opens, and the chum falls into the water. This attracts the ahi. The other half of the 'ōpelu has the hook embedded.

Now, all we had to do was wait. I got a soda from the cooler and lay back in the canoe. I had one leg dangling over the side, and I draped my line over the 'iako. The 'iako is the piece that attaches the outrigger to the canoe. I let the line run over the palm of my left hand. When I had a bite, I was going to know about it right away. I was warm and relaxed and feeling fine. Sweetie sat bolt upright at his end of the canoe trying not to doze off, a loose grip on his line. After a half hour or so, he suddenly jerked awake.

"Uncle!"

I sat up quickly. Sweetie's line was running through his fingers, and it had startled him.

"OK, now give'm some…"

Before I could say anything more, Sweetie jerked up on the line. And that was that. The line went slack, the fish and one of our precious hooks were gone.

"You gotta give'm slack, brah!" I was trying not to yell at him. I had a lot more to say, but suddenly my own line started to run. I let the fish take a little. The depth of the bait and the strength of the pull of the line told me it was a nice sized ahi.

"Big buggah!" I told Sweetie.

"*Auwē*, ride 'em, Uncle!"

I played the fish for a while, letting out line and pulling it in. When the fish was near the surface, I told Sweetie to get our gaffe ready, and he grabbed it from the bottom of the boat. Our "gaffe" was a baseball bat with a lead weight wrapped around the tip and a big ugly hook protruding from the end.

It took about 20 minutes before the fish tired and finally surfaced. I held the line while Sweetie gaffed him. We got him on board and laid him in the bottom the boat. I threw some ice from the cooler on the fish. Sweetie and I settled back in opposite ends of the canoe, facing each other. Then we started to laugh, I guess in relief and in triumph.

"Dat one big buggah, dat fish," Sweetie said.

"Dat's not one fish!"

"Look like one fish to me."

"Look like one new clutch to me."

Sweetie laughed.

"You right. And look like one big Christmas pahty for me and my friends. *Mele Kalikimaka*, Uncle!"

But it was time to get back to work.

"OK, put da line back in da wattah," I said. "We gotta catch some mo' fish."

We were in high spirits as we started to re-rig our lines. It was going to be a good day.

It was just past noon when we got back to the beach. We probably looked more like a maritime disaster than a floating canoe. We were sitting so low in the water, the 'iako was nearly awash as we made our way through the tricky shore break. Sweetie and I were singing at the top of our lungs, Christmas carols, and old Hawaiian songs. Sweetie didn't know many of the Hawaiian words, so he filled in the blanks with gibberish and laughter. When we got close into the beach, he gunned the engine and we ran the canoe up on the sand.

I was glad to see that a bunch of my young nephews and cousins were waiting for us. Arley had done his job, as usual. They ran over to give us a hand pulling the canoe up on the beach.

Lopaka was looking into the canoe. "Holy shit, Uncle!"

"Damn!" said another kid.

Seven 50 to 120 pound ahi packed in ice in a twenty four foot canoe are an impressive sight. Sweetie and I climbed out as the boys all gathered around to see what we had brought in.

"We goin' make one big Christmas pahty and all the guys in Kona goin' come!" Sweetie announced.

The young men whooped it up, slapping their new hero, Sweetie, on the back. I guess he was as proud as he'd ever been in his life. But we had to get the ahi onto fresh ice for the trip to the Suisan fish auction on the other side of the island. I reached into the canoe and hauled out a huge fish, picking it up by the tail and pulling it over my shoulder.

"We not goin' have one pahty, if the fish no get to Hilo."

Sweetie, a big grin on his face, leaned casually against a palm tee and let the others carry the fish to my cousin's truck. I grabbed our empty ice coolers and hauled them over to the trucks. I started loading the coolers with fresh ice, and I called to Sweetie.

"Eh! No only stand around, give me one hand."

Sweetie came over to help me carry the coolers. We set off in the direction of the canoe.

"Where we goin' with dis?" he asked me.

"Gotta load up for the next trip," I told him.

This stopped Sweetie in his tacks.

"Next trip?"

"Da fish still biting out dere. We go get some mo' before everybody else finds out."

Obviously it never occurred to him that we would be going out again. He was ready to spend the rest of the afternoon telling his cousins big game fishing stories and planning for his blowout of a party.

Lopaka saw that I was loading up the canoe.

"Wat, you guys goin' out one mo' time?" he asked.

"Plenny fish out dere still," I said.

"You sure get plenny fish blood in dat canoe. Sharks goin' come."

"Sharks, Uncle!" Sweetie said.

"Da kine, Liko, he wen come back one hour ago. He seen some sharks, fo' sure. He not goin' out again."

"Sharks are our 'aumakua. They're our guardian angel, brah. No need worry about 'em," I said. Sweetie was looking doubtful so I tried another tack.

"Eh, Sweetie and me, we not afraid of some sharks, right Sweetie?"

As the reigning hero, Sweetie had to go along.

"Shit, no!" he said. "Sharks no scare us."

He called out to the others, those less daring than us.

"Eh, give us one hand with dis canoe! We going back out fo' some mo'." With that bit of bravado, we launched our boat into the surf.

By mid-afternoon. The canoe was very low in the water again, with two 100 pound ahi in ice. I was napping and Sweetie was sulking. I think it had finally hit him that I tricked him into this second trip. We had one line in the water.

"Getting late, Uncle."

"Lissen, if you do what I say and not lose anotah hook, we be outta here by now."

"We no need some mo' fish."

I pointed to our catch. "See that big buggah ovah dere? Dat's my wife's new four piece bedroom set. Queen bed. Headboard. Six drawer bureau. Mirror. And dat other fish, just a little smaller? Dat's her new TV with remote control. And dis other one." I wiggled my hand line. "Dis one is one new Guild 12-string guitah. Dat's fo' me. We get dis one, den we go home. OK?"

"What if we don't get anotah one? We no have bite for ovah one hour. Suppose…" Our conversation was interrupted by a welcome tug on my line, the unmistakable feel of a good-sized ahi.

"Guitah calling me," I said.

For a couple of minutes, I worked the fish, the line wrapped around my hand. This guy was putting up a struggle. It was my last hook, and I had to be careful not to lose it or the fish.

Then, wham! — there was this huge yank on the line that nearly catapulted me over the bow of the canoe. Sweetie laughed, thinking I was clowning around. I quickly wrapped the line around the 'iako, and the bow was now pulled down into the sea, almost to the water line. Sweetie sobered up quickly.

"Wat the hell was that?" he wanted to know. I was wondering the same thing myself. Now I could see that the canoe was moving. We were being pulled forward.

"Start the engine!" I yelled to Sweetie. Sweetie gave the starter rope a pull, and nothing happened. He gave it another yank, and the old motor sputtered to life.

"Reverse! Put 'em in reverse!" I shouted. Sweetie put it into reverse and opened the throttle, but all this did was lower the bow further, and seawater started to pour in over the sides of the canoe. We were on the verge of sinking in dangerous waters, over a mile from shore.

"No, no, kill 'em, kill 'em!" I yelled. Sweetie shut down the engine. The canoe stabilized. We had taken on a lot of water. We have a couple of empty plastic syrup containers with a rope attached to the handle and the bottom cut off to form a scoop. We immediately grabbed these and started to bail. Glancing behind us, I could see that there was a wake behind our canoe. We were clearly being pulled forwards, and at a pretty good speed.

"Wat the hell is dat?" Sweetie's face had gone pale with fear.

"Ain't no sardine. Swallow that ahi whole, brah," I said, chuckling, with more courage than I really felt. Sweetie peered down into the ocean in front of the boat. Suddenly he pointed downward into the deep.

"Look!"

I looked down into the water, where a tiny gray fish was swimming along just ahead of our canoe. But our fishing line extended all the way from our boat to this "minnow." It was a trick of perspective: the "minnow" was a huge shark, deep in the clear blue water, pulling us along.

"It's one shark! Cut da line!" Sweetie yelled.

"Dat's da last hook!"

"Please, Uncle, you so pa'akikī. Cut da line, let's get outta here." Pa'akikī. Stubborn. Yeah, I guess that's me, sometimes. But this fish was making me angry.

"He's not getting my last damn hook."

"He's taking us away from land!"

I took my bearings, and sure enough, we were being pulled away from the island. I reached down in the canoe and came up with my home-made gaffe, and hefted it.

"What you goin' do wid dat?"

"Wait fo' him get tired. Den whack 'em on da head when he come up."

Sweetie looked at me in disbelief. Okay, maybe I wasn't being smart about this. But I wanted that guitar. To get the guitar, I needed my hook. All I had to do is get it out of the mouth of the large shark down below us. I settled back into the seat with the gaffe in my lap. I knew this might take some time.

Thirty minutes turned into an hour, and then another hour passed. The canoe was still being pulled along by the shark. The island shore was receding in the distance now, and the sun was much lower on the horizon. I sat with the gaffe at the ready. Sweetie was trying a new tactic, staring me down. It wasn't working.

"You *pupule*, brah," he finally said. I'm not crazy, though. That damn fish was not going to get my last damn hook. We kept moving south. I decided to tell Sweetie a reassuring story. I asked him if he remembered my *Tūtū* Koko'o, my father's grandmother.

"She *pupule* too," he let me know. I used to think so. So I told Sweetie my story. When I was a little guy, maybe three or four years old, my *tūtū* used to take me down to the sea once a month or so on the lava rocks near Kealia. She would pick up a couple of large stones and bang them together, over and over. Eventually, a huge dark shadow would appear in the water. A big shark. And she would start feeding him. She brought whatever she had to give him, usually *'ōpelu*, but sometimes taro, sometimes *'ulu*, cooked breadfruit, whatever she had on the stove in our cookhouse. She'd smile at the shark and chuckle to herself while she'd toss the food out to him. He would swallow the food whole, and swim in circles, looking for more. She'd always remind me that this was the "grandpa shark," the one with all the whiskers.

I was a little kid, and I didn't know any better. I'd never heard of a shark with whiskers and I wanted badly to see one. The shark would make pass after pass until the food was gone. She'd promise him she would come back soon. She would wave goodbye to the shark and make me do the same. And then she'd take my hand and lead me back on the narrow path up the cliff. Later, when I was a little older, and taking a cue from my big brother, I would just laugh at her when she went off to feed "grandpa." But I really missed those trips to feed him.

Sweetie was listening intently.

"So because I wen make fun of her she nevah take me to feed da shark again."

"How come she feed sharks?"

"You know, I always used to tink about that. I nevah find out fo' one long time, from Uncle Kamuela. You remembah him?"

"Yeah. Had white hair and one cane. I remembah."

"Uncle Kamuela wen tell me dat when *Tūtū* Koko'o was one young kid, she one *pupule* buggah."

"I believe dat."

So I told Sweetie the rest of the story: My uncle told me that back in the 1920's, when *tūtū* was around sixteen, she had been with the family, gathering *'opihi*, a small limpet that clings to the rocks above the sea. The ocean was rough that day, but when the swells receded, they revealed the wonderfully tender yellow-tinged *'opihi*, the ones you usually couldn't get. The ones further out of the water were green and crunchy, still delicious, but, *Auwē*!, those yellows were so good, eaten raw with Hawaiian salt and seaweed. You could only get them on the big wave days, 15 or 20 foot surf, when the *'opihi* would climb out of the water a little higher.

Anybody else would wait for a smaller surf day, and gather the *'opihi* when it was safe, but before they moved back down the cliff. Not my *tūtū*. She couldn't wait. She had invented her own system using a couple of 30 foot bamboo poles. One of the poles had a small net attached to the end. The other one had a putty knife tied on the end of it. Hanging out over the cliff, she would pry the *'opihi* loose with the knife on the pole and then flip them into the net on the other pole. She was leaning dangerously close to the pounding surf as she worked. Her mother called out to her to stop, but *tūtū* had to have those yellows. A stubborn young woman.

Nobody saw her fall, except her little brother. One moment she was there, reaching down over the cliff, and the next moment she was gone. "Sistah wen fall on da rocks," was all little Paloa could say. And she must have hit her head and been knocked unconscious, because she wasn't seen again. Some of the braver young men climbed down towards the water, to try to recover her body. But it was too dangerous with the big surf, and their families pleaded with them until they came back to higher ground. That night, she was mourned with the old Hawaiian chants, her grieving family sitting a vigil by torchlight on the top of the cliff. If she was still alive, the torches would be a sort of lighthouse to guide her home. If she was dead, they would be a beacon for her spirit to see.

They didn't return to the house until after dawn. *Tūtū*'s mother went in first, and a moment later everyone heard a shocked cry from within the house. They rushed inside to find an impossible sight: there was *tūtū* lying in her bed. She had a huge mark, undoubtedly from the fall into the rocks, from the left side of her face all the way down to her left knee, kind of like a big red birthmark.

Still disbelieving her own eyes, her mother gently touched her daughter, and *tūtū* opened her eyes. She was alive! It was a miracle. How did she get there? Had she not fallen after all? No, she said, she fell into the water and a shark, a "grandpa" shark with whiskers, carried her to a beach a couple of miles away. She swam to shore, and walked home. No one was there. Exhausted, she fell asleep, awakening to her mother's touch.

Her auntie wanted to clean her wounds, but *tūtū* wouldn't let her, insisting that they were marks of honor, not caused by the rocks, but by a slap from the shark. The "grandpa" shark. It became the standard family joke. From then on, *tūtū* wore her "shark" scar proudly. And she began feeding sharks, from that day until the end of her life more than 70 years later.

"So now you know," I told Sweetie, "Sharks are good luck fo' us." He almost seemed convinced. But it was sunset, and we were now miles from home, with the wind and the currents against us. We knew it was going to be tough getting back.

Just then, the line went slack. I leaned far out over the water, which scared the hell out of Sweetie.

"He's coming up," I said.

I stood up in the canoe and braced myself, holding the gaffe high over my head. My mouth was a little dry. Maybe this hadn't been such a good plan, but even cutting the line wasn't going to help us now. Still, I was determined, if there was a chance, to nail this guy and get my hook back. I must have appeared just a bit crazed, poised there, silhouetted against the setting sun, with this ridiculous looking weapon above my head. Sweetie was looking at me like I was a madman.

And suddenly, he was there, right next to the canoe. He wasn't the biggest shark in the sea, but he wasn't much smaller than our 24 foot canoe, either. He rolled his eyeball back, as sharks do to protect their eyes before they attack. I could see the whites of his rolled back eyes, and I knew he was getting ready to eat. His dorsal fin stood a good three feet out of the water, to our canoe's 12 inches. I got ready to bring my club down on his head. I waited for the perfect position for my blow.

That's when I saw the whiskers. This shark had a beard! But no, it wasn't a beard. It was dozens, maybe hundreds of fishing lines and streams of seaweed coming out of his jaws and mouth. It was only a moment, but I could clearly see lines made of sennet, the old coconut fiber used by Hawaiian fishermen many years ago. For an instant I flashed back to the time with my *tūtū*, feeding the sharks in Kealia.

Distracted by the memory, I hesitated an instant too long, and my opportunity was lost. It was all the time the shark needed to get himself under the canoe, his huge body rocking the boat. Sweetie had a death grip on the *'iako*, his face a mask of pure terror. The outrigger on our left came up and out of the water, and the canoe started to overturn. Unable to keep my balance, I fell towards the shark, turning in mid air and exposing the left side of my body to the shark. If I fell into the sea, I knew I was a dead man. But then his tail came up, and he slapped me hard from head to foot with his rough, barnacled body, knocking me back into the canoe. With a quick and fluid motion, he turned and dove deep, snapping the line at last, leaving Sweetie and me bobbing alone far out to sea at sunset in our tiny craft.

Six hours later, a little past midnight, we finally got back to the beach. The ice had melted long ago, and our catch was spoiled. My entire left side was bruised and swollen from the shark's rough slap, the scars of which I will bear the rest of my life. Sweetie hadn't spoken a word to me the whole time. He would never go fishing with me again.

I am a modern American who has flown high over the ocean at nearly the speed of sound, and I am an ancient Hawaiian, who travels slowly and low in the sea, not even as high as a shark's fin. I am contemporary Western man as surely as I am my old *tūtū*. I am as stubborn and reckless as she was, and I have seen things she has seen. And my connection to the lives of my ancestors is cemented further, as it has been over and over during the course of my life.

This happened in December, 1976.

KA IʻA
Danielle Kaʻiulani Kauihou

Another day in paradise. Blue skies above with rays of light sparkling through every now and then. I wander sleepily out of my dark hole and take a look around. Most of my neighbors are already up and searching for food.

I keep close to the ground, looking for the pink limu that is so ʻono to eat. I soon find it, swaying to and fro as if being blown by a gentle breeze. I nibble on the little tree and eat till my ʻōpū is full. I never eat all the way to the root because if I do, that pink limu will never grow back. Back in my grandparents' days, there used to be so many different types of limu. But because humans were careless and tore the limu out by their roots, those kinds of limu grow no more.

Not knowing what to do next, I go holoholo for a little while. Aaaah! I run and hide in the nearest cavern available. The brown and white spotted eel slithers out from behind some rocks, looking for prey. I surely don't want to be his dinner, I'm too young to die! I hope he goes away soon 'cause I don't want to stay in here forever! In a short time he leaves, finding a small squid to chase. I hate eels! All they want to do in munch on little fishies like us. They can be just like humans sometimes. Once when I was small, I got caught on a fisherman's hook. It hurt my mouth a lot, but I was so panicked that I hardly felt a thing. Lucky for me though, the fisherman said that I was too small and threw me back. Now whenever I see a silver sparkle in the water, I stay as far away from it as I can get.

Last night, I was talking to my Aunty Uhu, and she told me that in Keʻanae, not one eel can be found living in its reef. She said that once there was this big fish who got tired of watching so many baby fish lose their lives to eels that he became an eater of eels. Well, he cleaned out that whole place and even though he's long gone, no eels have ever dared to return. I just might take a vacation there one time. I've never been outer island, but my friends tell me it's the greatest.

The other day, my friend Humu told me that there was a northwest swell coming in. I thought that there would probably be a surf contest, so I journeyed down to the shorebreak to see what was up. Sure enough, Manini and Hīnālea were wrestling in the shorebreaks. Sometimes I just sat under the rolling waves and watched wave after wave pass me by. It's always entertaining to see someone get caught in the bowls and watch them tumble over and over with the waves. Watching the playful humans is also fun. They look so funny trying to ride waves like us. They always fall off their boards.

The dolphins were always the best surfers. They ride so gracefully and make surfing look so easy. They're the most beautiful creatures I've ever seen. I'm just a small Mamo—a flicker of blue and silver in the vast blue sea.

But I don't care if I'm small, just as long as I'm a big fish in Kole's eyes. She's a beautiful combination of gray, white, and black. We met on New Year's Eve. Every year, the humans come out to Mākaha beach to catch the first wave of the year. They wear glow-in-the-dark necklaces and bracelets, making it seem as if there were such a thing as swimming fireflies. Anyway, there must have been a surfer who lost his bracelet, because there it was, lying on the ocean floor. Kole was near it, and the glow that reflected off her face awed me. She seemed to be radiating some beautiful form of light, and this drew me to her. Well, eventually we "hooked" up (maybe "hook" is a bad word, but you get the point). There are a lot of people who are against us being together, but we don't care. I guess that's because we were raised to mate only with our own kind, but this is LOVE!

Sometimes I wonder why there are so many different types of fishes in the sea. Then I realize that there must have been fishes like me, willing to risk their reputation to be with a fish of another species. Their children came out as hapa fishes, and that's where we all came from. I wonder why everyone doesn't know that?

Being a fish in these modern days is difficult. It's always a "survival" thing. I know I'm part of the food chain, but come on. There are a lot more good foods to eat. Besides, we have millions of tiny little bones that can kill you (hint, hint).

All right, so maybe we are delicious. But we deserve a break. We deserve rights too. We deserve a say in who gets to be eaten and when. I just want to live, maybe even travel. So please, remember that we're people too!

REDRAWING THE BIG ISLAND

Jeanne Kawelolani Kinney

Pele, the Hawaiian Goddess of fire
has no use for black sands anymore,
decides to magician it back into hot lava,
headstrong and sullen, she has summoned
the town of Kalapana back into her arms.
At night, the island glows, grows past
the boundaries of old *National Geographics*,
cutting maps into useless paper
adding latitudes and longitudes
into brand new numbers.

The houses have burned into land.
The crowds gather, their silent eyes
watch the muscle of heat shift
and create, inch the island bigger
than yesterday, smaller than tomorrow.
This growing is patient, moves beyond
the atlas that tries to confine land to books,
beyond the way tourists try to take pictures
of something they think they see —
I was there when the volcano erupted!

Hawaiians know how useless it is
to tame eruptions onto film,
the eyes of our hearts say, don't
just look, *see*. We know new land
is unruly, an adolescent blowing off steam,
slamming doors to emerge centuries later
smooth-skinned with lines intact,
filled out, and smiling through
wild orchids and passion fruit.

No National Park can contain this woman
who scribbles self-portraits red and black
against the earth, holding up her work
to say *here is more for you,* ignoring
the critics and agnostics who miss
the point of fire. *Let this burn a hole
into your memory,* she says,
I am too busy with revisions to be stilled.

LOʻI KALO
Makia Malo

In the early morning,
A bouquet of winds
Swirls above the loʻi kalo.

One, like a Kuewa, a wanderer,
Rambles aimlessly
Coming in low to the ground
From one side.

From another side,
The wild gypsy wind, makani ʻĀhiu,
Streaks downward
Stirring hearts of leaves
That flail in commotion,
Myriad hues of rippling green, dancing across the loʻi.

Makani Hoʻohani, a taunting wind,
Teases and flirts with the kalo
That bob and teeter coquettishly in its wake.

And sweeping down the slope of the mountain
Is makani Lena,
A cold wind from the south,
A rush of fragrant ginger.

Sea winds invade the land
With sprays of lipoa,
The strong distinctive smell
Misting the air.

The kalo are planted firmly upon their mounds,
Each puʻu, an island,
Moated from the others by
Icy cold,
Crystalline clear,
Upwelling water from an artesian spring.

They are rooted deep, the kalo,
In this land of our kupuna,
Sucking lustily of the honua, the earth.

I tread upon a bank of the ʻauwai,
The ʻauwai that flows
Among the loʻi kalo.
This is a gentle walk.

I pause,
And the pungent smell
Of wet, raw earth surrounds me.
Damp earth, slippery beneath my feet,
Squishes
As I reach forward with my toe
To touch the water.

Oooh . . . it is cold,
So cold, this early
On a morning still emerging from the night.

I hate the cold.
I shiver at the thought of what comes next.
As I walk
To the place
Where the day's tasks will begin.

Images of back-bending work
With the sun beating down
On backs already stinging with sunburn;

Images of toiling in freezing water until sunset,
Of hands and feet turned white and wrinkly,
Too exhausted and cold
To wash the mud from our ears and hair
Before going home
At the end of the day.

And always the cold
The relentless, unforgiving cold.
This will be a hurting walk
To that first step
Into the water of the loʻi.

I know I must not hesitate,
Yet I do.
I know I must be bold
To overcome my dread,
The shock of water so piercing,
So cold.
Still I don't.

I hate the cold,
But I fear Mama's wrath more,
Her angry eyes,
The set of her jaw.

Now I think of all the work that must be done,
Weeds that need attention,
Two rows of taro to be pulled,
Their beds rebuilt, new huli planted,
Encroaching grasses
Sickled away from the edge of the ʻauwai.

I start.
I take the hurting walk.

THE BEACH AT NAPALI
Leialoha Apo Perkins

Ioane could see the West Maui Mountains on one side and the beach on the other, from the kitchen window, between stained, red checkered curtains that flapped in the wind. The beach rolled like a white rug beside the deepening blue ocean. It was edged, landward, with blossoming pink *pohuehue*. The blossoms ran from the distant black reef, where the planter Tomlinson's residence stood, silent and aloof, to the cocoanut trees that straggled to the kitchen doorstep. It was Ioane's first day home in Napali after forty years.

Out on the bay, on an escarpment of exposed reef, *limu wawae 'iole* glistened like glass among strips of loose, green plankton. No one was in sight.

"Sis," Ioane called. "I goin' take a walk." The screen door groaned at opening.

"Kimo and t'em no wake up yet, Ioane," his sister called back.

"Oh, I no goin' see 'em. I goin' take a walk."

"A *walk*?" his sister repeated. She chuckled. "Boy, you jes' like da haole tourists, fo' shuah. You change'."

The screen door slammed shut.

The beach lay white and silent, excepting for the rolling surf and the wind. "This is how I used to think it was," Ioane said to himself, "and here it is: it's real. To think I couldn't remember it, when standing at Times Square and thinking, because people said so, that the world was passing by. The world! At Times Square!"

He laughed quietly. He braced his body into the wind. The waves roared. The surf broke. The wind shifted, suddenly, and he was pushed forward, where he had been pushed backward. He looked up. The sun, like a Cyclops, looked down. Tufts of clouds floated like a magically moving beard across the face of the sky. The wind shifted again. It bit into Ioane's shirt, sculpturing it to his torso. It whipped his pants around his legs, marking his long bones.

"For real," Ioane said again to himself. Then he began to laugh— incredulously, at first, and then, hilariously. He threw his hands out. He turned himself in the wind like one offering himself for inspection. The ocean roared. "Real," he shouted at the sun. But the wind squandered the message over the sand.

He began to run, feeling the wind in the crook of his back, as he moved backward toward the Tomlinson's house. He threw his head back. He felt the warmth of the sunlight on his face like a moving hand healing. The wind flung whorls of sand at him. It lashed his hair in his eyes. But that didn't matter.

"All those years that I wasted in New York, holding onto the standup straps of the subway, plying the uptown-downtown Manhattan underground: the squalor, the soot, the ear-splitting noise of the trains grinding to a halt, the graffiti on the walls, the stench of old urine, and the eyes—the cold, impersonal eyes with mouths to fit: small mouths, tightly clipped; big, thick-lipped mouths, temporarily slack from their feeding; gummy mouths holding together the emptiness of a toothless head; the small, impersonal hatreds and the personal hatred wrapped with caring possessiveness. One builds up a tolerance for the ugly, the demeaning. Why did I ever go away?" Ioane asked himself. "Worse, why did I *stay* away?"

The fact was: he did not care to know about it now. He didn't even know why there was a question after all these years. He looked up at the sun. It had not moved. He laughed at himself.

Just then a dog, a West Highland white terrier, barked. It ran towards Ioane and then past him into the breaking wave. It barked furiously at the curl of surf. Blanketed, it was swept off its feet, turned over, and then set down gently on all four legs. The dog wagged its wet, bristly-haired tail, barking deliriously at the next coming wave. When the surf touched it, the dog was standing, its tail ramrod straight. The dog jumped, was picked up, rolled over, and dumped onto the sand. The terrier struggled to its feet with strings of seaweed muzzling it. It pawed loose the seaweed. The seaweed rolled away in the backwash.

Suddenly the dog looked up. Its body froze. Its tail, which had been slapping the water, stood upright, its wet, bristly hair half straggling over the pink skin like a tattered flag in forlorn salute. The dog began to whine. It tucked its tail between its legs. The next wave broke over it, hurling the dog shoreward. It picked itself up, shook itself, and ran directly towards a man who was standing alone on a slight rise of a dune above the pink *pohuehue* blossoms high on the beach.

The man was dressed neatly in white shorts from which protruded two powerful swarthy legs, deeply tanned. Over his eyes, the man wore dark, round sun glasses. He had not called the dog. He had said nothing that Ioane had heard. Yet the dog had run to the man. It had run to him in a kind of hobble, its tail between its legs. Just as it was about to reach the man, Ioane saw what lay in the stranger's hand.

It took just the slightest movement, perhaps only a flick of the wrist. Something curled like a snake in the air and wrapped itself around the body of the terrier like a velvet ribbon. The dog whined shrilly, then whimpered. It crawled on all fours until its black nose, grubby with sand, and its wet, hairy paws touched the man's feet. Then it began to lick the man's feet, moaning rhythmically between each lick.

Ioane put his head down on his chest and held it, with his breath, as he walked, the wind in the small of his back.

"You back a'ready?" his sister cried out in surprise. She looked at him. He looked at her. Pin curlers tightly rolled left spots of her pink skull exposed. He and she had both grown much older than even he had thought. She was silver-haired—he had seen that, at the airport—but it had then struck him as something close to a kind of charm. Now he saw her nearly bald with pin curlers and vastly more wrinkled than he had ever seen her before.

Ioane looked out the window again. The dog and its owner were gone. In one corner of the glass pane window, he caught a glimpse of himself between the flapping oil-stained, red checkered curtains. His hair was white, almost beach white, even though his skin was as taut as perhaps the day when he had left Napali forty years before.

What he had left behind him long ago, he now remembered, was a longer memory of a snake whip in the hands of a sugarcane plantation *luna*. Like a string of delicate, black lace, the whip was wrapped over the sweating brown body of his father who was lying shirtless in bed, sweat pouring from his forehead, perhaps from the fever that he had been weathering for days, and his mouth open, soundless, and pink in a gasp.

Ioane thought of Times Square, now, with its traffic of human bodies manipulating about while high above everything, in teletype lights, ran the New York Times "All the News that's Fit to Print."

"Yeah," Ioane said, finally, to his sister. "The beach nevah change."

HE HUAKAʻI KAʻAPUNI MA HAWAIʻI
(RAMBLE ROUND HAWAIʻI)
from Mary Kawena Pukui
edited and translated by Mary Kawena Pukui and Alfons L. Korn

Kū e hoʻopiʻo ka lā
Ka lā i ke kula o Ahu-ʻena
Komo i ka laʻi o Kai-lua e —

ʻO Kona:
ʻO Kona ia i ke kai malino
Ke hele la i waho o Kapu-lau
Kani ka ʻaʻo i Wai-ʻulaʻula
A he alanui e waiho nei
A ke kanaka e hele ai la

ʻO Kaʻū:
ʻO Kaʻū ia, o Kaʻū kua makani
He ipu kai Pōhina nā ke Aʻe-loa
Lele koaʻe i Kau-maea la e —

ʻO Puna:
ʻO Puna paia ʻala i ka hala
Keaʻau ʻiliʻili nehe ʻōlelo i ke kai
ʻO Puna ia la e —

ʻO Hilo:
ʻO Hilo ia o ka ua kinakinai
Ka ua mao ʻole o Hilo
He ua lū lehua ia nō Pana-ʻewa e —

ʻO Hāmākua:
ʻO Hāmākua ia o ka pali Koʻolau
Ke kuʻukuʻu la i ke kaula
Ke ʻaki la ka niho i ka ipu
I ka pali ʻo Koholā-lele
ʻO Waipiʻo, ʻo Wai-manu e —

'O Kohala:
'O Kohala-iki, 'o Kohala-nui
'O Kohala-loko, 'o Kohala-waho
'O Pili, 'o Ka-lā-hiki-ola
Nā pu'u haele lua o Kohala

Ramble Round Hawai'i

The rising sun travels in an arc
reaches the flatlands of Ahu-'ena
enters Kai-lua's gentle landscape

   This is Kona:
coastal Kona along the unruffled sea
where the sun rides ahead to Kapu-lau
where cry of the puffin-bird at Wai-'ula'ula
breaks the silence of the traveler's trail

   And here's Ka'ū:
Ka'ū of the wind-swept back
where Pōhina's a pungent dish in the salty wind
while shining leapers at Kau-maea
soar like *koa'e*-birds through the air

   And Puna:
where *hala*'s fragrance blows from Puna's branching bowers
and pebbles at Kea'au whisper to the sea
Puna's forever there

   With Hilo:
Hilo of perpetual rains
rains in a never-clearing gusty sky
scattering the fringed *lehua* of Pana-'ewa

And Hāmākua:
Hāmākua of the windward Koʻolau hills
where the traveler lowering himself by rope
grips the net of his carrying calabash between his teeth
descends the cliff at Koholā-lele
and those sheer-sided valleys Wai-piʻo and Wai-manu

  Kohala last:
lesser Kohala, greater Kohala
inner Kohala, outer Kohala
and then Pili and Ka-lā-hiki-ola
companion hills traveling as a twain

A NOTE ON THE TEXT

The chant was sometimes recited for its own sake, but it could also be performed as a string game. The various figures were manipulated so as to suggest a panorama of changing landscape as seen while traveling counter-clockwise from one to another of the six ancient districts of the island of Hawaiʻi.

HE MELE HE'E NALU
(A SURFING SONG)

collected by N. B. Emerson
edited and translated by Mary Kawena Pukui and Alfons L. Korn

Ka nalu nui, a kū ka nalu mai Kona,
Ka malo a ka māhiehie.
Ka 'onaulu loa, a lele ka'u malo.
O kaka'i malo hoaka,
O ka malo kai, malo o ke ali'i.
E kū, e hume a pa'a i ka malo.

E ka'ika'i ka lā i ka papa 'o Halepō
A pae 'o Halepō i ka nalu.
Hō'e'e i ka nalu mai Kahiki,
He nalu Wākea, nalu ho'ohu'a,
Haki 'ōpu'u ka nalu, haki kuapā.

Ea mai ka makakai he'e nalu.
Kai he'e kākala o ka moku,
Kai kā o ka nalu nui,
Ka hu'a o ka nalu o Hiki-au.
Kai he'e nalu i ke awakea.

Kū ka puna, ke ko'a i uka.
Ka mākāhā o ka nalu o Kuhihewa.
Ua 'ō ia, nohā ka papa!
Nohā Māui, nauweuwe,
Nauweuwe, nakelekele.
Nakele ka 'ili o ka i he'e kai.
Lalilali 'ole ka 'ili o ke akamai,
Kāhilihili ke kai a ka he'e nalu.

'Ikea ka nalu nui o Puna, o Hilo.

A Surfing Song

The big wave, the billow rolling from Kona,
makes a loincloth fit for a champion among chiefs.
Far-reaching roller, my loincloth speeds with the waves.
Waves in parade, foam-crested waves of the loin-covering sea,
make the *malo* of the man, the high chief.
Stand, gird fast the loincloth!

Let the sun ride on ahead guiding the board named Halepō
until Halepō glides on the swell.
Let Halepō mount the surf rolling in from Kahiki,
waves worthy of Wākea's people,
waves that build, break, dash against our shore.

Now sea-spray of surfing looms into sight.
Craggy wave upon wave strikes the island
pounded by a giant surf
lashing spume against a leafy altar, Hiki-au's temple.
At high noontime this is the surf to ride!

Beware coral, horned coral on the shoreside.
This channel is treacherous as the harbor of Kākuhihewa.
A surfboard smashes on the reef,
Māui splits, trembles, sinks into slime.
Many a surfman's skin is slippery,
but the champion of chiefs skims into shore undrenched
by the feathery flying sea-spray of surfriders.

Now you have seen great surfs at Puna and Hilo!

LAVA WATCH
Marjorie Sinclair

1.

The lava began to flow seven years ago and everyone talked about it. An appearance of Pele—her will, her power. No one thought to mention the danger to our village huddled under the green in the fragrances near the sea's edge; our village so old no one had heard when it began. Pele was—well, Pele: dictatorial, implacable. We listened to surf, not lava.

My whole body, however, quivered with that plume of smoke up the mountain and the red night flares. I smelt the lava seven years ago—a light sulfur odor mingling with faint fumes of burnt earth and burnt leaves. People said I was crazy. They said you couldn't smell those things so far down the mountain slope, and especially so near the sea.

Through the years the lava moved on with a leisurely insistence. It had a secret pace. Who could tell what was going to be: how far the molten rock would travel? Only Pele. Goddesses seldom reveal their thoughts. Their moods speak only at moments of action—unless they are in a prophetic mood. Pele was a goddess of action—a sudden appearance, clothed in fire.

On the mountain slope the lava has left a huge irregular trail of darkness, a trail of the burned and engulfed. People have moved from their burned homes hunting new lives wherever they can find them. Now the lava is at the village: relentlessly moving as if it had all the time in the world, its huge curling paws touching into flame everything in their way.

During those seven years, I passed my 70th birthday and two of my daughters left their husbands and moved back home. I reared a grandson who called my house home—whenever he was there. Samuel was a rascal boy, full of city ways. I wanted to give him the old country ways. He was always restless. He wouldn't stay. He was like a bird. The lava brought him back for a while, and he hiked through the woods to where he could see it, sometimes camping for several days. Of course he wasn't supposed to do that, but he was expert at escaping notice. I finally decided that I mustn't worry about him. Or even ask him where he went. I guess I can't blame him too much for his mercurial behavior. My parents thought I was that way when I was young. After all, I had disappeared into California for a while. I wish I could be that way now, flitting from place to place. But I'm stuck here sitting around with old age, with the girls, Piilani and Harriet. And the lava has almost reached my back door.

2.

Piilani was impatient with her mother's attitude toward the coming of the lava. Mom didn't want to do anything. Couldn't she see the inevitable? Couldn't she feel it in her bones? She simply drifted serenely from day to day, acting as if the lava moving down the mountain were a stream of water. She watched the houses burn. Afterwards she embraced her old friends, her neighbors, and cried with them; she even gave them shelter for a night or two. She was, however, tranquil and steadfast. And she wouldn't allow anyone to remove her things from the house. "The time has not come," she said. Yet the lava was almost up to the old stone wall great grandpa had built long ago. The pond in the back yard had turned brown and seemed almost to be boiling. The water heaved, mud churning up from the bottom.

"Look, Mom, your pond is turning to lava," Piilani said. Red anger was in her face. "It's time. For god's sake, it's time!"

Keahi looked beyond her daughter at the stark lava softened by the green foliage of the plumeria and hau trees. At some moment the leaves and fronds would burst into torches. She was sure the trees knew by now. Just as her father and grandfather in their graves in the side yard knew. Grandfather always said: Pele gives and Pele takes away.

Harriet the younger daughter embraced her. "Mom, you're a little confused. I don't blame you. Why don't you let Pii and me take charge?"

Keahi returned the embrace, then broke away from Harriet's arms. She had her plans, very simple ones. But she wouldn't tell her children until the first paw of lava touched the house. Maybe not then, if she could manage.

"I'll go inside now if you want and look things over." She saw the brightening in her daughters' faces. It made her sad. "Some things I'll leave, the junk things."

In the living room she touched the pieces of old koa furniture. She laid her hands on the big table which had been polished by three generations. It was silky to the touch. She picked up one of the poi pounders from the shelf and saw, as she had so many times, her grandfather sitting in the back yard pounding poi on the big board. He had thin legs, a little pot belly and a head of thick white hair. She always thought it looked like seafoam. Long ago the board had disappeared. Now poi came from the market. She smiled slightly: change, change in everything—people, plants, even the shape of the mountain and the shore. Only the lava remained in its ancient ways, oozing or pouring from craters and vents as it made its slow passage, the trail of Pele down the mountain.

She went to the bedroom and lay down. These days she was often tired.

Especially since the lava had come close. It was the unhurried pace of every-thing, the uncertainty; and she had to admit it, the anxiety. She hated anxiety. She knew exactly what would happen. When? That was what she asked as her heart beat irregularly and her breathing was heavy. She felt as if the lava were pulsing in her, a part of her. Sometimes she wanted to be part of it, treading slowly, stretching, breaking into red coals and flame: a moment of celebration. Afterwards, always a black collapse, a dark settling down.

"Hey, Mom, Mr. Lee is here." Tommy Lee was from Civil Defense. He had spindly legs like grandpa and teeth too big for his face. He was a good man. Very sympathetic, very tough, very fair. He walked into her room.

"Hello, Tommy, want something to drink?"

"No thanks. I came to see if you have made plans. I figure another 48 hours."

"You usually figure right."

"Thanks, Keahi. I ought to know. But then you can't always be sure."

"I'll get some boxes and start packing. The girls are pretty much packed. I think their friend is bringing a truck today."

"That's good. What about you?"

She laughed. "What about me? Well, what about me?"

"Your safety is my job."

He was a little pompous, she thought.

"Okay, save me." She flung out her arms.

He smiled and gently slapped her elbow.

3.

The truck has come, the house is full of people, confusion, noise. I'm out near the wall. The lava touches it in places. Intermittent snake tongues of flame reach out. Shrubs fire up and fill the air with smoke. The black paws seem reluctant to climb our small wall. They puff in redness, shoot out orange and blue, then collapse into darkness. The lava has its own voice—it crackles, even a roar that becomes a tinkling sound as momentary cooling begins. It is its own thing.

I remember the first time I smelled the lava. It was the 1935 flow up be-tween the mountains. It was cold and the air pricked my nose. Still the lava smell was warm like sun on rock on a hot day. The fumes were sulfuric. The cold air muted everything. Down here by the sea the salty air mingles with the lava; strange odors, bitter and choking, filter through the air.

"Mom, where are you?" Harriet is bellowing. She's always had a raucous voice, deep as a man's. She's like a man, aggressive, demanding. At the same time she's beautiful in a large sort of way. Like her father, big eyes and glossy hair.

She knows perfectly well where I am. There's no place to hide. She likes to yell. That's all.

She is suddenly standing next to me. Her face is sweaty and her t-shirt stained with dust and grease. The outline of her breasts is round and strong. "Mom, where's your stuff? You haven't even started yet!"

"I'll get to it in my own time. Don't worry."

"The point is you have to follow the lava's time. It's going to burn us down."

"Hush, girl." I dread their rage, their resistance. Piilani's just the same. They can't accept what they can't control.

"Your time," she snorts. "We know what your time is. Well, it's your own problem."

She's back in the house and I'm alone again. It's good being alone. I like peacefulness. Before the lava came so close, I could lie down and have a nap. No one asked if I was okay. I could sit in a chair and rock, letting images of the past swarm before my eyes. I could even see the days in San Francisco before I gave up and returned to my village. For many years I never doubted my decision. Only in these last seven years I have. And I don't understand why. Could it be that I too hate the ravaging, uncontrollable lava, spoiling everything? All the changes, new plans for life; and just at a time when I want to settle down, sink a little into the green and the earth. Why should it happen? A simple technical answer. Tommy says we're in a rift zone. Sooner or later there would have to be lava. I chose village life with the possibility of a fire I had forgotten was living under that earth.

More than fifty years ago I walked up and down San Francisco streets with their hard cement, cold wind plastering my clothes to me and the shadow of tall stern buildings. In the afternoon the fog always came in. The fog helped a little, blurring the hard rectangular edges of things. I yearned for soft air, sea sound, the clatter of coconut fronds.

But more than that I yearned for people: the village people, taking things as they come, living in the moment, the day—not always looking to a future which would take place at an unknown time, maybe never. If they were angry they shouted. If they loved, they hugged each other. If they were hungry, they ate. Of course they didn't much like change. Or the strangers coming in and trying to take their land and imitate their ways. They suffered, on occasion, from a somber melancholy.

In San Francisco I was becoming somebody else. I decided she wasn't what I wanted to be. If I had stayed there I would be crisp, business-like, money-minded, looking to the future. It might have been a good thing. I had a first-rate job. Everyone wondered why I suddenly resigned and went home. Who can say why now? Exactly why? I did it and that's all. Now the village for which I yearned is being devoured. And I don't have that whole other life I never lived. And so I go round and round as I did all those years ago. There will have to be another life. What?

"Hey, Mom!" This time it was Pii. "You can't stay here until the fire strikes the house. You've got to get your stuff together."

"Look, Pii, the lava has almost reached the top of the wall over there by the hala tree. You remember, we buried poor old Brownie under that tree."

"You talk like you're pupule. What are we going to do about you?"

"Just let me be crazy."

"Don't you understand the danger? After all the burned houses?" she muttered impatiently. "You should have stayed in San Francisco."

I was startled. Had she read my mind? I couldn't stop the tears. She put her arms around me. "I'm sorry," she said.

"What you said is good. The way the lava is good. Bursting through old, forgotten blocks."

4.

It's dark. Tommy comes to tell me that only this night is left. Tomorrow is the deadline. He asks if I need help—he'd send some men. I tell him no and kiss him on the cheek.

I can hear the lava rustling and belching along the wall. In one place it has gone over and a fat finger reaches toward the house. Darkness flames at moments from burning gas or burning trees. I get up and put some clothes in a bag. I hunt in the dark along the shelf of artifacts for the small stone bowl, once a lamp, and the small adze with a sharp edge. I hunt for the calabash my grandmother gave me. She had patched it in the old way. That's all I want to take. The other bowls, the poi pounders, the books and old fishing weights can stay. The furniture can stay. The refrigerator and stove, the rugs. I want to give them all to the lava, to Pele. She wants the village. It's hers. It's always been hers.

I walk around the house trying to fix myself in it forever. I, Keahi, forever in this old wooden house buried in lava. Of course the house will burn. It won't be a house—just a place where a house was. But the poi pounders might remain. And the fishhooks made of bone. Most things are fragile. Like this mountain slope continuously changing, like this very island with fire in its belly. With Pele.

It is dawn. Samuel is standing by my bedside. I ask him where he comes from and he says Australia. I don't ask why he was in Australia.

"I heard our house was going to burn. I came to get you."

He pulls me from bed and puts my old robe around me. "Come on, Tutu, or Tommy will be after you."

We hurriedly eat some left-over poi and bits of cold fried fish. He makes steaming coffee.

He opens the kitchen door wide so we can watch the lava. It has reached the oldest plumeria tree. One paw stretches toward the garage.

"It's an octopus," I say.

"Eh, Tutu, you always make fancy talk. No need wash the dishes. The lava will."

Tommy Lee shouts from the front door. "Hurry up, you two."

Samuel takes my two small bags and ushers me toward the door. "You go ahead," I say.

He gives me a questioning look.

"I'll be coming. Don't worry."

I had remembered my kukui nut necklace. Papa made it for me. During his last years when the sadness settled on him and he drank all the time, he polished kukui nuts. One day he wrapped a strand of white kukui in a ti leaf and gave it to me. It wasn't for a birthday or a celebration. He just gave it to me and shuffled off to his little room in the shed. That night I wore it when we ate. He smiled. I was fourteen at the time. He died a year later.

Samuel shouts from the door. "I'm coming to get you."

"No need," I answer.

I take the kukui nuts from my drawer and join the two on the lanai. Samuel puts his arms around me. His pick-up truck is out there on the road. Tommy's van is there. No sign of the girls.

"I want to watch," I say.

"Okay, if you let Sam take care of you," Tommy says.

They don't trust me. They have wild fantasies. I'm a mad old woman. Oh no, I whisper. I'm just Keahi at the moment when my house begins to burn. And I'm still inside. I put myself there last night. I'm inside with all the others who have lived there. I'm inside with all the thoughts I had in San Francisco—and after I came home. My life, quiet, drifting, is there, each moment of it moving into every other moment in the fire.

I grip Samuel's arm. The house is incandescent with flame—only its dark skeleton shows. The roof is crashing, the fire shouts and roars. I'm glad I left all those old things for it to have. The lava can take them away.

Samuel helps me climb into the truck. "The girls didn't want to watch," he says. "But they knew you would want to."

The house is taking a long time to go. Heavy smoke lingers, shadowing everything. It smells like wood and rock and garbage burning. I can't feel anything, I'm empty. It's frightening. Only my eyes watch the end of the house. The rest of me is somewhere else.

I turn away and put a hand on Samuel's thigh. "Where are we going?"

"Like we planned. The girls are at Aunty's, waiting."

"I don't mean that!"

Samuel races the engine of his car and starts off with a lurch. "Yeah, where the hell is any of us going?"

NATIVE PLANTS
Rene Sylva

The Hawaiian plants are social plants.
If you go look underneath the Hawaiian tree
there's all kinds of plants that grow under them.
Ferns and vines and shrubs and other kinds of trees.
They all grow together under the Hawaiian tree.
But the non-native plants are antisocial trees
like the kiawe or the eucalyptus or the ironwood.
Go down to the beach sometime and look at
the ironwood tree, the mature ironwood tree,
nothing grows under there.
They don't like anybody else except
for one species, their own kind.

TO HEAR THE MORNINGS

Haunani-Kay Trask

To hear the mornings
    among *hāpu'u*: a purity
of cardinals, cunning bees
    in shell-covered sleeves
        of honeysuckle,
           . . . the aqua undertones
        of cooing doves.

To seek our scarlet
    'apapane, Hōpoe restless
        amongst the *liko*
           and *'ōlapa* trees,
        shimmering the leaves,
        . . . *shush-shush*
           of burnt rain
               sweeping in from Puna.

To watch our lustrous
    volcanic dawn seducing
        'elepaio, speckled beak
    sucking *'ōhelo* berries
        oozing sap
           under a crimson sun.

To breathe the Akua:
    lehua and *makani*,
        pua and *lā'ī*,
           maile and *palai*,
           . . . pungent *kino lau*.

To sense the ancients,
        ka wā mamua—from time before
    slumbering still
        amidst the forests
            of Ka'ū, within the bosom
                of Pele.

To honor and chant,
    by the sound
        of the *pū*, our
    ageless genealogy:
'āina aloha,
    'āina hānau,
        . . . this generous, native Hawai'i.

RETURNING TO WAIMĀNALO

Haunani-Kay Trask

between two worlds
shorelines of meaning form
edging closer, farther
marking the one space
where all my selves
cease transforming

war continues on one side
from the other beckons
a different front:
all battle, scarred
and scarring
two worlds, two
world wars

but here, there is a moment
a fall of light along
the shore, gleaming
a changing shoreline
this is not peace, or
solitude. i am too
unseasoned for that

it is something strange:
intelligible space
in a bitter universe
rhythm amidst terrifying noise
human need that does not
suffer

it is my experience
when struggle wanes

myself, and my people
absorbing sounds
near a silent sea
forming ancient
contours of meaning

excerpt from

EDDIE WOULD GO

Bryan Hiroshi Wake

CAST: James
              Andrew
              Randy
              Barry

JAMES Eh. I know one good story from when he was one small kid. You like hear 'em?

BARRY & ANDREW Shoots!

JAMES K-den. Now da Aikaus had one big family. Six kids. Wit dat many kids foa feed, da family nevah have planny money foa buy toys oa bikes. But dat nevah mattah. Dey had da ocean. Eddie faddah, Pops Aikau, wanted foa make shuah all his kids could swim good. So he went teach 'em himself. All at da same time.

ANDREW Six kids? All at da same time?

BARRY How he went do dat?

JAMES I show you.

(*JAMES looks through the trash can and pulls out an Aloha shirt. He puts it on.*)

JAMES Eh boys! Let's get going! Wake up already!

BARRY How come you talking li' dat, James?

JAMES My name not James. I Pops Aikau. Eh! Boys! Wake up! Whea Eddie? Eddie? Brah, who goin be Eddie?

BARRY Oh! Me! Me! I Eddie! What we doing today, Pops?

(*JAMES tosses the shorts to BARRY.*)

JAMES We going beach.

BARRY Beach? Jeehaa! Whea my board, Pops? I like surf.

JAMES Surf? Eddie. You no can even swim yet. Go wake up yoa braddahs.

BARRY Ok . . . pops.

JAMES Eh . . . yoa voice kinda low for one little kid. Make 'em highah.

BARRY OK daddy.

JAMES Highah.

BARRY OK Daddy!

JAMES Das bettah Eddie.

BARRY Eh guys! Wake up! Daddy taking us beach today. Uhhh daddy? Who dis?

JAMES You no recognize yoa own braddah? Das Gerry.

(*JAMES gets a bandana from the trash can and throws it to BARRY. He puts it on ANDREW.*)

ANDREW Eh! Dat ting was in da trash can!

JAMES Brah, just play along.

ANDREW Oh man . . . Wheee! I love to go beach!

JAMES C'mon boys. Carry my surfboard.

(*JAMES hands them his surfboard. They struggle to hold it up.*)

RANDY Eh. What about me?

JAMES Oh . . . look, boys. You left yoa little bruddah Clydie all alone. He goin cry you do dat. Hea Clydie. It OK. (*JAMES gets a hat from the trash can and puts it on RANDY. He makes him suck his thumb. He turns the bench away from the audience.*) Come, boys. Look. (*They join him. He motions the audience to make the waves again.*)

BARRY Wow. Big da ocean.

ANDREW Look real deep too.

JAMES Remembah boys, you show her respect, an she always goin take care of you. OK?

BARRY & ANDREW OK, Daddy.

JAMES All right. You first Eddie.

(*JAMES tosses BARRY over the bench. He flails around on the floor.*)

BARRY Aaahhhh! Daddy! Why you trew me in da ocean?! I dunno how foa swim!

JAMES I know. Good time to learn!

BARRY AHH! Somebody help me! I goin' drown!

JAMES You not goin' drown boy. Relax!

BARRY AHH!! (*He points to the audience.*) Get big, ugly fish in da ocean! I getting tired! Daddy! I getting tired!

JAMES 'Cause you yelling so much! Calm down Eddie. She take care you.

BARRY I going die!! I goin die! I goin . . . goin . . . eh . . . eh . . . wow.

(*BARRY begins to float.*)

JAMES See. What I tole you? How you feeling now Eddie?

(*BARRY starts to swim.*)

JAMES OK Gerry, you next.

(*JAMES tosses ANDREW over the bench.*)

ANDREW Huh? AAAHHH!! Help me! I dunno how foa swim!! I goin drown! I goin drown! . . . I goin . . . eh . . . eh! I swimming!

(*ANDREW swims and plays with BARRY.*)

JAMES Clydie. Your turn.

(*JAMES picks RANDY up and tries to throw him in. RANDY clings to JAMES. He wraps his legs and arms around him.*)

JAMES C'mon Clydie. Let go of me. Look. Yoa braddahs like da watah. Let go of daddy. Let go of daddy. Ehh! Let go of me!

(*The bench topples over and RANDY and JAMES fall in the ocean. The boys laugh and play in the water. They climb up the bench and dive into the ocean. JAMES stands above them.*)

JAMES OK. Next lesson. We going learn how foa surf.

(*JAMES shows the three boys his surfboard. They gasp. JAMES places the board on the bench. BARRY, ANDREW and RANDY jump on the board, laughing and fighting. JAMES gives them a stern look. They stop celebrating. He motions to get off the board. They quickly do.*)

JAMES You tink das surfing? Look. Look at da ocean first. What you see?

ANDREW Watah.

JAMES What you see in da watah?

RANDY Notting.

BARRY No wait. Wait. I see something. Look like one bump on da ocean. Eh, dea annoddah one.

ANDREW And one noddah one behind it! Yeah, I see 'em.

RANDY Eh. Da bumps coming closer daddy. Stay coming right at us!

JAMES Yep. Watch now. Dey goin turn into waves. Watch. Watch. Dea.

BARRY, ANDREW & RANDY Whoa.

BARRY Dat was unreal!

JAMES Get on yoa board. Kneel on top. Dea you go. And paddle out. Paddle. Paddle. Hea yoa line up. Now sit up. You see da bumps? You see dem coming in again?

BARRY Dea! Dea dey stay!

JAMES I'll tell you when to start paddling. Wait. Wait.

RANDY Da bumps getting kinda big, Daddy.

JAMES Not yet. Not yet. Now! Paddle! Paddle! Geev 'em all you got! Paddle! Paddle! Da wave goin run you ovah you no paddle fastah! Go! Go! Dea! You got 'em. You riding da wave! You riding da wave!

BARRY, ANDREW & RANDY . . . whoa.

(RANDY looks terrified; ANDREW looks amazed. BARRY has the biggest smile on his face. JAMES tilts the bench. The surfboard angles down towards the floor.)

RANDY What happening?! What happening?!

JAMES Da wave starting foa break! Stand up! Stand up! Put one foot in front. Bend yoa knees. Get yoa hands out. Balance. Balance. Hold! You goin slide down da face!

(*The boys yell in excitement, awe and fear.*)

JAMES All right! Next lesson!

(*JAMES tips the bench even more. The boys fall off the surfboard. JAMES makes them roll and tumble on the floor.*)

BARRY What happened? What happened?

JAMES You just went wipe out.

BARRY Oh, no way!

JAMES No talk! You undah watah! Da wave holding you down. Hold yoa breath. It throwing you all ovah like a rag doll! All you see is white all around you. Bubbles. Swirling in every direction. You no can see. Hold yoa breath! You running out of air. You gotta swim to the surface. Wrong way. You went hit sand. Hold it. Wait foa da wave to pass ovah. Wait. Wait. Now swim up! Swim to da surface! You running out of air. You running out of air. You not goin make it!

(*The boys swim to the top of the bench. They exhale together, coughing and wheezing. They lie on the bench, exhausted.*)

JAMES Good job boys! Good job! Eh! Nevah turn yoa back on da ocean. I no care how tired you are. Das bettah. Good. Eddie? What wrong?

BARRY Da surfboard. Whea da surfboard?

JAMES Right hea. Why?

BARRY I like go again.

ANDREW Hah? You went almost die.

RANDY You crazy Eddie.

BARRY But didn't you see it? Da ocean was moving all around us. Water churning, splashing everywhere, like it was alive. And I was riding on top of it! Come Clydie! We go again!

PONO

'AU 'A 'IA

Mary Beth Aldosa

Kumu sat on the steps leading to the stage at the Diamond Head end of
Lehua School's cafeteria, the large wooden *pahu* drum completely filling
the space between his legs. Despite opening the room's six swinging doors
to their widest point, the air in the caf was hot and still. The breezes that
usually wafted in to cool our *halau*'s dancers seemed hesitant, not wanting
to enter tonight. Was it the *pahu*'s presence or some other source of tension
that hung in the air? The wind seemingly sensed what we *haumāna* knew: we
were doing drum dances tonight. Hula was not going to be fun.

I threw my bag onto one of the cafeteria's long white tables, pulling my
blue calico *pā'ū* skirt over my work clothes. Everyone, it seemed, was in a
bad mood, and I soon discovered it wasn't entirely because of the drum.

"Da nerve, yah? Dat haole kid. You saw him on TV? Fricken atti*tude*!!"
said Tanya, in disgust.

Jan's laughter spilled over into her words. "Das fo get cracks! And mo
worse, braddah is on the football team! You *know* he goin' get lickens."

"It's not really the kid," added Cathy in her high-class pidgin. "It's the
mutha. Hel-lo!! It states right on the application, BI-O-LOGICAL grandparents!"

I slid into line as Kumu let his thick hands fall simultaneously onto the
drum's sharkskin surface.

"Alright, let's get started," Kumu called, pulling his drum closer to him.
He lifted his hands again, pounding out familiar rhythms with the graceful
hands of a dancer:

Oo te te te, oo te te.

Oo te te te, oo te te.

Kumu took us through the basic steps of the hula, calling out each new
movement with perfect and practiced timing, "Hela . . . 'ami . . . 'uwehe . . .
kāwelu . . . *kāholo* . . ." Correcting his dancers, reminding and prodding us to
push further, bend lower, fully extend the arm, the foot, the leg, all the while
pounding out a steady drumbeat.

Oo te te te, oo te te.

"Girls, push out your *kīkala*!"

Oo te te te, oo te te.

"Flatten your foot, Malia."

Within minutes of "basics" my leg muscles began to ache and stiffen. My
T-shirt, wet with sweat, clung to me and I struggled to catch my breath. Still,

with calves that felt as though they were on fire, I repeated *hela* after *hela*.

Oo te te te, oo te te.

Finally, the drumming stopped, but our relief was short lived. "Alright everyone. Take a second, then we'll get started on *'Au 'A 'Ia.*"

Oh Lord! Not 'Au 'A 'Ia?! Just the thought of the dance's strenuous movements tired me. Dancers left their lines to grab water bottles or a bit of fresh air, stretching stiff limbs and trying to return their breathing to normal.

"Whoa! Extra long warm-ups, and now *'Au 'A 'Ia*? Okay, which one of you guys went piss him off?" joked Alina, one of Kumu's old-timers. We giggled softly, which Kumu must have taken to mean that we had had enough of a break because he called us back to dance.

"Alright," Kumu began. "Who remembers what *'Au 'A 'Ia* means?"

Even before most of us had fully processed Kumu's question, Yaeko was calling out the answer. At sixty-two, Yaeko was our oldest dancer and she knew all the answers. She studied every song, memorized every movement. While other dancers spent their breaks smoking cigarettes or talking story, Yaeko would diligently study her hula book. She'd taken hula for years and practiced daily. Despite her efforts, Yaeko was not considered a beautiful hula dancer. Still, what she lacked in gracefulness she more than made up for in knowledge and heart. The *halau*'s younger dancers didn't appreciate this about Yaeko, but I did.

"Be . . . ah . . . steen-a-gee," she said, in her thick Japanese accent.

"Be stingy. Very good, Yaeko. Ladies, it was a warning, remember? A warning, to hold on to our culture, our way of life. Now, this motion." Kumu lifted his arms to shoulder height, extended his hands out toward us, and crisply and deliberately flipped them . . . palms up, palms down, palms up, palms down. Flip, flop, flip. "What is this motion supposed to signify?"

Finally, a question I could answer. "Turmoil," I said softly.

Kumu nodded. "*Maika'i*. Yes, the flipping of the hands represents turmoil. Remember now, this chant comes from a prophecy that things in Hawai'i were going to change. It was foreseen that people would come here, to these islands, and the change they brought would leave us in turmoil." He dropped his hands and looked at us. "Ladies, I expect to *see* that emotion in your dance."

Kumu walked back to his drum and sat on the steps facing his dancers. He raised his hands and let them fall. A series of low, loud thuds resounded through the room. I stood still, and felt my breath coming harder and faster, not from exertion since I had not moved a muscle, but rather, from rage. Frustration at the week's events, at Judge Ezra's decision to allow a non-

Hawaiian into Kamehameha School, flowed through my veins, feeding each cell with a rage I rarely allowed myself to feel. The anger moved, danced to the *pahu*'s beat, a slow moving lava flow, deadly and unforgiving. Kumu Kula called to us, readied us for the dance.

"*Ae, 'Au 'a 'ia e kama e kona moku . . . 'Au 'a!*"

Weeks of conditioning had trained our bodies to respond almost automatically to Kumu's call, his *kāhea*. Hips began their slow circular motion, an *'ami* to the right that, once completed, was then reversed, becoming an *'ami* to the left. *Right . . . reverse, left . . . reverse*, the body moving, circling, dancing in an imitation of life: Hawaiians taking the same path but going nowhere, rounding a corner only to be pushed back. My heart pounded as I forcefully pushed and pulled at the air, grabbing, grasping. But for what? The motions were repeated, driven by the slow beat of the *pahu*, that with each repetition grew faster and more bombastic.

" '*Ai ha'a!*" Kumu commanded loudly. "You need to '*ai ha'a*! Bend your knees!" The drumbeat came to an abrupt halt as Kumu stood.

"All of you," he said, "Do this motion." We obeyed, imitating Kumu's hand placement, our right fist firmly sitting on our left.

"Now, from here, I want you to twist and push down."

Twist . . . push down. Twist . . . push down. Kumu observed the movement, still unhappy with its execution.

"No, that's not quite it," he said, more to himself than to the class. "Look, ladies, I need you to visualize. Think of someone you can't stand. Now, take your fists and make a wringing motion . . . like you're wringing their neck! Have you all got a person in mind?" Kumu asked mischievously.

Oh yes, Kumu, I thought. I have a perfect someone in mind . . . a certain maha'oi haole *from Kaua'i . . . a certain lying, non-Hawaiian "mutha" who sneaked her smug little brat into Kamehameha School . . . a certain scheming, lying little thief.*

Kumu made his way back to his drum, raised his hands, and let them fall with a thump. Right on cue, the dancers commenced, but within seconds, Kumu's drum fell silent again, bringing the dancers to a halt mid-motion. Our frustration manifested itself in the strange looks that passed between us. *What had we done wrong this time?*

Kumu stood up and walked out from behind the *pahu*. "Ladies," he said, a look of exasperation on his face. "*Think* about your dance. As a dancer, you need to think! What are you saying?!" His question lingered in the air. *What are we saying, I thought.*

"You folks wanna know what I see?" Kumu asked. "This is what *I* see."

He took what vaguely resembled the correct body position, his erect arms slackening, falling just an inch or two. His fully extended leg had been repositioned, bent as a prostitute on a street corner might do to attract a customer. And his hands had changed as well, converting from the desired harsh, stiff-fingered movements to the soft, languid hand movements that people generally associate with hula. Kumu repeatedly flipped his hands, a soft, gentle flip, smiling as he did so. *Palms up, palms down, palms up, palms down. Flippity, floppity, flip.*

Kumu spoke calmly. "When you do your motions to *'Au 'A 'Ia* like this, this is what you are saying." When he spoke again, the pitch of his voice was higher and decidedly feminine, as were his mannerisms. *"Howzit . . . you like my land? Go 'head. Take 'em . . . How 'bout my cah? You like my cah too? Hea . . . hea da keys. Eh, by da way, you like come Kamehameha School? Come! It's all yoa's. Halp yo'salf!"* Kumu's stunned students erupted with laughter, as did he.

Finally, Kumu composed himself. "Ladies, that is not the message we want to send! We need to be strong, be stingy, *'au 'a 'ia* . . . we need to hold on! Let's try it one last time."

Kumu returned to his place on the steps, his tired hands and eyes rested on his *pahu*, as he lifted his hands and let them fall once more. Raising his eyes, he looked over the *pahu* at us, his voice poised to *kāhea*. And then I remembered. Kumu . . . our beloved kumu who gave so much of himself, who sought to empower his students through the dance, who unlocked the mysteries of our *kūpuna* . . . our revered Kumu was not Hawaiian.

The commanding boom of the *pahu* startled me, and when I began to dance, I was a half-step behind the others. I felt Kumu's eyes on me as I struggled to catch up to the class, to find my place in the dance, but in that split second, I had lost my focus. I paid dearly for my inattention, as all dancers do, for even as I danced, even as I grasped, pulled, and twisted, I felt it. In desperation, I reached out and tried to cling to it, but my rage, the rage that had once fueled my dance, continued to slip away from me. *I can't do this, Kumu*, I thought. *It's just not in me.* I danced in spite of the tears that were intent on coming, wanting only to dance through the pain and disappointment, wanting desperately for the dance to end.

When the final drumbeat sounded, it was Alina who spoke first.

"Kumu," she panted, "We could use a break. Whoa! Dat dance is killin' me!"

Kumu smiled and nodded silently, freeing his dancers to leave their lines. Most headed to the lanai outside the *makai* doors. I always preferred the quiet and dark of the *mauka* side of the building. I headed there and leaned my back against the cool metal of one of the lanai's orange poles.

The material of my *pā'ū* skirt helped smooth the way, as I slid down the pole to the concrete floor and sat, in the cool blackness. The voices of my fellow dancers seemed distant, and for tonight I wanted to keep them there. I needed to be alone, to feel my own feelings, to know my own heart, not someone else's.

From where I sat, I could see the entire room. I watched silently as Kumu reverently lifted his *pahu* and gently placed it in the center of a large square piece of faded green fabric. He bent down to gather the cloth's four corners, wrapped the drum's sides, and tied the opposing corners into a knot, binding them tightly together. He slid his hands between the knotted fabric and the drum's surface, lifting the *pahu* from its place of honor at the room's center to a less prominent location off to the side. I heard Kumu's voice, lighter now, call to his *haumāna* to return to the room. It was time to begin the *'auana* portion of the night, the hula numbers that we always looked forward to. I watched as my fellow dancers lined up, but I couldn't bring myself to join them. I still had not fully recovered from *'Au 'A 'Ia*. I turned back to the night, and thought about Kumu, about the dance he had chosen for us, about a mother from Kaua'i and her son. What was it that I was supposed to take from tonight? What was the lesson?

I finally realized that, for me, *'Au 'A 'Ia* can never again be just another dance. It is a reminder, my reminder, to stay vigilant, for change is coming, and it will keep coming. From a chant written over a century ago, generations before my mother and her mother before her, came a message from our kūpuna, as real and true today as it was then: *'au 'a 'ia* . . . hold on to your culture . . . hold on to your traditions . . . *'au 'a 'ia* . . . be stingy. And Kalena Santos, the mother from Kaua'i, source of the hurt and anger running through the Hawaiian community right now. What of her? Perhaps she was put in our path as a reminder as well . . . to remind every Hawaiian that the threat to our people is real. It lives and breathes and walks among us every day. The names will change, the faces will change, but they will always be with us. Which brings me to Kumu. He is a reminder as well, a loving reminder that not all non-Hawaiians will try to take from us. Some will love us, nurture us, and empower us. Some like Kumu will help us find our way back to our past, to the wisdom of our ancestors, without asking for anything in return but our love and friendship.

"Meri Bet? You okay? Kumu send-a me to check on you." It was Yaeko. I smiled at her through my tears, and nodded. She extended her hand, and I took it gladly. Then she pulled me to my feet.

UNCLE'S DRUM
Kimo Armitage

Uncle go to Makaha Beach, darktime
and jams on his drums.

Aunty lets him go,
check out his creative side, besides
so romantic.
All her friends jealous.

    "Learn to play something,"

they tell their fat husbands.

Beach People always ask:
"Eh, what you playing?"

Then. Polite kine.
"I can play too?"

Then they try act. But,
nobody good like Uncle.
'Cause he get plenty
fruh-stray-tion.
He just play, and play, and play.

Then one day, police men come, and
take his music away. They throw,
"You bodering people," at him,
until he believe it.

    "Come over here again, and we'll put you in jail."

So he went one noddah beach.
And play. Soft kine.
Soft *kine*.
Until
he no can handle,
and play real loud again.

Then other people came.
And brought their drums.
And ukuleles.
And maracas.
And spoons.
And they made a band.

When Uncle comes home,
he plays with his kids.
He go to work.
He love Aunty like teenager.
But, the cops find the new music.

Then he no go no more.
"No need," he say.
"Too much trouble," he say.
"Too much fruh-stray-tion," he say.

But sometimes, I see him
looking out the window.
Tapping his fingers—small kine.
When no one looking.
Seeing music dance on the windowsill.

. . . AT HEART

Kahi Brooks

Aloha
poor ting, her
bus' up
used up
spread too thin
people from all around the world
think they know her
think they carry her in their hearts
they all call her
Ahhlooooohaaaaaaaaaa!
and take her name in vain

HAWAI'I PONO'Ī

Puanani Burgess

On Friday, August 7, 1987
Forty-three kanakas from Wai'anae,
In a deluxe, super-duper, air-conditioned, tinted-glass
    tourist-kind bus,
Headed to Honolulu on an excursion to the Palace,
    'Iolani Palace.

Racing through Wai'anae, Ma'ili, Nanakuli—
Past Kahe Point, past the 'Ewa plain—
In the back of the bus, the teenagers—35 of them
Rappin', and snappin', and shouting to friends and strangers
    alike: Eh, howzit, check it out, goin' to town . . .

(Along the way, people stop and stare, wondering,
    What are those blahs and titas doing in that bus?)

Cousin Bozo, our driver, (yes, that's his real name)
Spins the steering wheel, turning the-hulk-of-a-bus,
Squeezing and angling it through the gates made just
Wide enough for horses and carriages and buggies.

Docent Doris greets us:
"Aloha mai. Aloha mai. Aloha mai.
"Only twenty per group, please.
"Young people, please, deposit your gum and candy in the
trash.
"No radios. No cameras.
"Quiet. Please."

"Now, will you all follow me up these steps.
Hele mai 'oukou, e 'awiwi."

Like a pile of fish, we rushed after her.

At the top of the steps,
We put on soft, mauve colored cloth coverings over our
    shoes and slippers,
        to protect the precious koa wood floors
        from the imprint of our modern step.

Through the polished koa wood doors, with elegantly etched
    glass windows,
Docent Doris ushers us into another Time.
Over the carefully polished floors we glide, through the
    darkened hallways: spinning, sniffing, turning,
        fingers reaching to touch something sacred, something
        forbidden—quickly.

Then into the formal dining room, silent now.
Table set: the finest French crystal gleaming; spoons,
    knives, forks, laid with precision next to gold-rimmed
    plates with the emblem of the King.
Silent now.

La'amea 'U.

Portraits of friends of Hawai'i line the dining room walls:
    a Napoleon, a British Admiral . . . But no portrait of
    any American President. (Did you know that?)

Then, into the ballroom,
Where the King, Kalākaua, and his Queen, Kapi'olani, and
    their guests
        waltzed, sang and danced and yawned into the dawn.
        (No one daring to leave before His Majesty)
The Royal Hawaiian Band plays
    the Hawaiian National Anthem and all chattering
    and negotiating stops. As the King and his shy Queen
    descend the center stairway.

And up that same stairway, we ascend—the twenty of us.
Encouraged, at last, to touch . . .
   Running our hands over the koa railing,
   . . . we embrace our history.

To the right is the Queen's sunny room . . . a faint
   rustle of petticoats.

To the left, we enter the King's study:

   Books everywhere. Photographs everywhere.
   The smell of leather and tobacco, ink and parchment—
   The smell of a man at work.

   Electric light bulbs (in the Palace of a savage,
   can you imagine?)
   Docent Doris tells us to be proud, that electricity lit
   the Palace before the White House.
   There, a telephone on the wall.

   Iwalani longs to open those books on his desk,
   Tony tries to read and translate the documents,
      written in Hawaiian, just lying on his desk.

La'amea 'U.

Slowly, we leave the King.
And walk into the final room to be viewed on the
   second floor.
The room is almost empty; the room is almost dark.
It is a small room. It is a confining room.
   It is the prison room of Queen Lili'uokalani.

Docent Doris tells us:

"This is the room Queen Lili'uokalani was imprisoned in
for nine months, after she was convicted of treason.
She had only one haole lady-in-waiting.
She was not allowed to leave this room during that time;
She was not allowed to have any visitors or
communications with anyone else;
She was not allowed to have any knowledge of what was
happening to her Hawai'i or to her people."

Lili'uokalani. 'U.

I move away from the group.

First, I walk to one dark corner, then another,
        then another. Pacing. Pacing, Searching.
        Trying to find a point of reference, an anchor,
        a hole, a door, a hand, a window, my breath . . .
I was in that room. Her room. In which she lived and
        died and composed songs for her people. It was
        the room in which she composed prayers to a
        deaf people:

        "Oh honest Americans, hear me for my downtrodden
        people . . ."

She stood with me at her window;
Looking out on the world, that she would never rule again;
Looking out on the world that she would only remember
    in the scent of flowers;
Looking out on a world that once despised her,

And in my left ear, she whispered:

'E, Pua. Remember:

This is not America.
And we are not Americans.

"Hawai'i Pono'ī."

Amene.

REMARKS
REGIONAL CONSTRUCTIONS OF CULTURAL IDENTITY FORUM
July 6, 1997
Puanani Burgess

'Ano'ai me ke Aloha, e nā hulu manu like 'ole.

In our mothers' tongue, "Greetings among us, birds of many feathers."

I'd like to say a couple of things first. One, when I began writing poetry, it was not with any audience in mind, nor any poet in mind. Those poems just had a life of their own and, in my present life, I'm beginning to find the meaning in them. They are probably my greatest teachers.

I want to start off by reading a poem and telling a story to show you, as an example, how poems and stories are very necessary tools in regard to community organizing, especially in these times. The poem I'd like to read to you is called, "Choosing My Name."

> When I was born my mother gave me three names:
> Christabelle, Yoshie and Puanani.
> "Christabelle" was my "English" name,
> My social security card name,
> My school name,
> The name I gave when teachers asked me
> > For my "real" name; it was a safe name.
>
> "Yoshie" was my home name,
> My everyday name,
> The name that reminded my father's family
> > that I was Japanese, even though
> > my nose, hips and feet were wide,
> > it was the name that made me acceptable to them
> > who called my Hawaiian mother *kuroi*;
> > it was a saving name.
>
> Puanani is my chosen name,
> My piko name, connecting me to the 'Āina,
> > and to the kai and to the Po'e Kahiko;
> > it is my blessing and my burden,
> > my amulet, my spear.

When I first wrote that poem, the place it first appeared was in one of the special editions that the newspaper puts out and my father saw it. That was the first place that he saw that poem. My father is Japanese. I was named after him. His name is Christopher Yoshiyuki Sonoda and I am Christabelle Yoshie Puanani Sonoda.

My father was immediately called by my aunties and uncles asking him, "Who is she writing about? Who are those people that called her mother *kuroi*?" And, "You know, you need to call her up and tell her to stop doing that. It's not right that she talk about family stuff in the newspaper."

My father, much to his credit and a feature, I think, of his own courage that I never recognized growing up, said, "That is the girl's history and she deserves a way to tell that history and however she wants to tell it. It is her reality." And so, with those words, he kept them from ringing me up and disconnecting me forever.

I was thinking about a title for this talk and if I had one it would be something like "Finding Meaning in the Face of Power: The Role of Poetry and Storytelling."

What our communities are undergoing right now is incredible pain. They are being asked to transform themselves without any input. We see golf courses, we see all kinds of stores and developments that are cropping up in our community that have no relationship to who we are.

There's this really wonderful old woman who I met in Wai'anae Store; she came up to me and said, "Eh, Pua, you know what . . . I live Wai'anae all my life and you know, I born hea and I come this store every day and I know everybody. But you know, I come this store now and I know almost nobody and I nevah move!"

That is the reality of what is happening in our communities. If you have the price of lease or rent or mortgage, you can become a neighbor. But just living next door to each other doesn't make you a "neighbor," not in the old sense, like in the days of our grandparents. Part of the reason why it is so hard to be neighbors is that we don't have Time. Families are working themselves to death. They are working one, two, three jobs. Both adults are out there. And there is not time just to sit back and create those neighborhoods that each of us who are fifty years old and older really understand and have experienced.

And so we're thinking about how we can talk about and retrieve our history, not just in terms of celebrations or memorial events or dry essays, but how do we retrieve our history as the people in Appalachia, who are some of my greatest teachers, have done. The people of Appalachia are also trying to recover their history and dignity in the face of tremendous disempowerment and oppression. They are trying to find the meaning of the coal mine experience, for example, just as we are trying to find the meaning in the plantation experience.

Poetry has been essential in people being able to back into their pain, to be able to deal with very painful issues in a way that doesn't destroy them. That poem, "Choosing My Name," talks about some very difficult issues of identity, security, values and oppression.

I used to watch those mah jong games, you know, that our aunties and uncles and grandparents played. Sometimes it was *hana-fuda*, but for my Japanese aunties and uncles, it was mostly mah jong that they played. They all gathered at one auntie's house, and at some point they would talk about my mother. And I was a little child just hanging around and they would call her things—like *kuroi*—what they actually meant was "nigger." And they would wonder how Yoshibo could have married that woman. And, as a child they dismissed me, not realizing that I had ears and a heart and a mind and that someday, those memories would become part of my politics.

But as you look at me today and as I look at myself in the mirror, I am Yoshie, I am that Japanese girl that grew up with my *bachan* and *jichan*. I am the girl that went to *bon* dance and went to the temple to bless those little pieces of tissue paper that my grandmother used to paste on me to bless me and to protect me from hurts. I am that person as well.

I am also Christabelle. I am that American girl who grew up pledging allegiance to the flag and singing those American patriotic songs with tremendous loyalty to that country. And then I discovered that my loyalty was misplaced and a whole range of people, not just Hawaiian people, are discovering actually what happened in 1893 with the United States Government. And what do you do when you are faced with a history that you never knew, never understood? History that was not part of yours and that you are learning about as an adult. History that causes tremendous pain.

I want to tell you a story that shows how to deal with these issues. History is—and I think the Japanese have also found this to be so because of the role of Japan in the war—that history is part of reclaiming our health, as a society. If we cannot reclaim our history, live it, own up to it, do something about it, then we continue to be victims of that history.

I have a very good friend who teaches Hawaiian history at Pearl City High School and she is a Japanese woman and every time she comes to that part in Hawaii's history that deals with the Māhele, which is the great cutting up of the Land and the distribution of that land to a variety of interest groups—every time she comes to that part, the Māhele, she sees the kids doing this: they put their heads down on the table, make pepa airplanes, fly 'em around the room, talk to each other, absolutely zone out of that discussion.

So, what she found out, after seven years of teaching that course, was that the kids believed, "Eh, my people stupid! If dey wasn't stupid, how come dey no moah da land? Dey shoulda regista for da land, just like da law tole 'em foa do. But no, dey nevah do 'em. Dat's why we no moah land, no moah watah, no moah money, no moah powa."

And, you know, nothing you or that teacher could tell them could talk them out of that reality. They live in the projects; they know what poverty is; they live it. They understand hopelessness. And there's nothing we can say to dissuade them. They don't buy the statement, "Hey, you can grow up to be President of the United States. You can be anything you want." That's not their reality.

So, on the first day of school, she had a genius idea; it was a simple idea, as most truly genius ideas are—what she did was she wrote up on the blackboard, you know, in that place that teachers really like, on the far, far upper right corner, she wrote, "Register for your chairs in two weeks, or lose it." And then she signed it and then she drew a chalk box around the sign.

Two weeks later, the kids came into the classroom, looked around and said, "Eh, teach. Like whea da chairs?"

She said, "What do you mean, 'Where are the chairs?'"

"Like, what we goin' sit on? Floah?"

"Well," she said, "You read English?"

"Yeah."

"You read the sign that I put up on the blackboard?"

"Yeah."

"Well, why didn't you register for those chairs, like I told you to do?"

"Yeah, but you nevah tole us, 'Eh, pay attention, dis foa real.' Nobody wen evah do dis to us befoa; so, eh, we wen jus' blow 'em off."

"Well, now do you understand what happened to your ancestors?" she asked. "They were being asked to register to own the land; it was like being asked to own your own mothers. How many of you have the audacity to go down to the Bureau of Conveyances to register to own your mothers? Your ancestors were not just being asked to do something unusual; they were being asked to do something sacrilegious—to own land. They were also being asked to do this at a time of great imperialism in the world and in the Pacific. Back then there were no empowerment workshops to tell the people about their human and political rights. No, nothing like that was going on."

So, those kids began to understand that within the context of the world in which Hawai'i existed, that there were many things that were happening that was not caused by the stupidity of their ancestors. So, they began to pick up their history as a spear and began poking holes in all the paradigms that imprisoned them.

Whenever I tell that story, to all kinds of people, they begin to understand that we need to reclaim our deep history. In one of the projects that's part of our community called the Cultural Learning Center at Ka'ala, every year we work with about 3,000 kids, ALL kinds of kids, ALL makes and models. And one of the things that we teach there, the most important thing, is that the 'āina, the land, is color blind. She doesn't know if you are Japanese, Chinese, Hawaiian or haole. She only knows if you love her; she knows if you respect her. And when you treat her as all mothers should be treated—with dignity and respect—then she gives you back that dignity and respect by giving you food, shelter, stability and Life.

And so when we talk to kids and we tell them, "Don't give us that bull that you're not responsible for the Land because you're not Hawaiian; you are responsible. This Land is your Mother, as well as mine. But it goes beyond that, this history is yours to care for, not just mine; the future of Hawai'i is your responsibility as well as mine.

In ending my presentation of how poetry works in the face of power—it becomes an incredible part of how our whole society reorganizes itself around certain values—I want to read a poem that I wrote called, "The Mouse Is Dreaming." The last lines of this poem are actually an old Eastern European saying.

> In the dark hole behind the washing machine,
>> the house-mouse is dreaming.
> Whiskers, body, tail—twitching and trembling,
>> paws scratching the air.
> That mouse, he's a dreamin'
>> of great chunks of cheese, and whole loaves of bread;
>> of a nest made of the finest pieces of cloth and paper,
>>> dry, warm and snug.
>> Of living out in the open once again, to be sun-warmed
>>> and star-shined.
>> Of walking. Of walking through the territory patrolled by the Cats;
>>> of cat traps, and cat cages,
>>> and cats without claws and teeth;
>>> Of a world without Cats.

And this mouse, she's a dreamin'
    of acres of lo'i kalo, of nets full of 'ōpelu,
    of rocks choke with 'opihi and limu,
    of forests of koa and 'iliahi and wiliwili;
    of empty and crushed buildings which no longer
        scrape the sky;
    Of living in the open once again, to be sun-warmed
        and star-shined;
    Of walking. Of simply walking through the territory
        controlled by the Cats;
        of cat traps, and cat cages,
        and cats without claws and teeth;
        Of a world without Cats.

And the Mice dream dreams
    That would terrify the Cat.

Aloha.

excerpt from
SUPER SECRET SQUAD
Lee Cataluna

CHARACTERS: Wanga
                        Togo
                        Boy
                        Duck
                        Liko
                        Kaleo

PLACE AND TIME: O'ahu – now

ACT I
SCENE III
WANGA Okay, okay, you guys getting all excited. I mean, I like the idea of public service and using our powers for good . . .

TOGO Screw that. Let's use our powers for bad.

WANGA But what exactly are we talking about doing here?

BOY Menehune stuff.

TOGO Radical stuff.

LIKO Cultural activism.

DUCK Stuff that involves beer and duct tape.

LIKO So what's our first mission?

DUCK What's the most egregious wrong being done to our people?

LIKO Whoa, take your pick. Illegal overthrow, ceded lands, the price of Frosted Flakes.

DUCK What's the most egregious wrong done to our people that can be fixed by five guys and a roll of duct tape?

BOY Well, that's a shorter list.

DUCK You know it, Wang.

WANGA Are you serious?

DUCK As a myocardial infarction.

LIKO You think we can pull it off?

BOY You guys talking about what I think you guys talking about? You know what I talking about?

LIKO So what, Togo. You in?

TOGO Only if it involves the use of explosives.

DUCK Then it is decided.

BOY Shoot! The Modern Day Menehunes! Cannot go wrong!

Duck, Liko, Togo and Boy exit. Wanga faces the audience.

WANGA We decided to make our move on Labor Day. State holiday, so we figured the Wendells of the world would be busy weeding the yards outside their town houses in Mililani. We small-kind borrowed some overalls from one painting company in Mapunapuna, stocked up on duct tape, and picked up a load of World War II era explosives from Ducky's grandfather's garage. The last piece of equipment we brought was Liko's idea. At first, we thought was kinda' stupid, but it turned out to be our secret weapon on this, our first strike.

SCENE IV
Kalakaua Avenue in Waikiki. Duck, Liko, Togo and Boy enter wearing the overalls. Boy brings one for Wanga to put on. Boy is carrying his ukulele case. Liko carries a clip board.

LIKO A clip board gives you instant authority. It's a western cultural thing.

TOGO So the cops come to arrest us, what you going do? Take your clip board and whack them over the head? Ooh, I scared of you.

DUCK Focus, men. We're on a mission.

WANGA (*to the audience*) Ducky had the whole thing drawn out. On graph paper with mechanical pencil, no less. He made us memorize the plan and then eat the paper. I made Boy eat mine. In fact, I think Boy ate all the papers. We probably should have been scared, but it was like we knew what had to be done. So we just stuck to Duck's plan and set out to right the biggest wrong that had been done in Hawaii in our life time. I mean, the biggest wrong that could be fixed by five guys with duct tape, some damp gun powder and a clip board.

The lights come up on a bronze man wearing shorts and no shirt standing atop a pedestal with his arms outstretched. His back is to the audience.

LIKO Duke Kahanamoku with his back to the ocean.

DUCK Sacrilege.

BOY Yeah, how would they like it if we made one statue of, like, Abraham Lincoln sitting down on the job.

WANGA Uh, actually, Boy . . .

LIKO Never mind, brah, he's rolling with it.

DUCK Soldiers, take your positions.

Liko and Boy act as lookouts. Duck takes explosives out of Boy's ukulele case and sets them at the base of the statue. He gives the detonator to Togo, who sets it off with great glee. Then, just as Togo and Wanga start to turn the statue around, Boy jumps as if being questioned by someone.

BOY Oh, howzit officer. How you doing? You looking the statue? Us too. Nice yeah? Braddah could swim, no?

LIKO (*jumps in*) Uh, what we doing? Uh, we doing routine maintenance and adjustments on a public memorial statutory item. Why? What you mean under what authority? We get authority. We from the City and County Department of Statue turn-arounding.

Wanga steps in to help.

WANGA We have joint jurisdiction with the State Department of Statues, Monuments and Signs.

LIKO It's a new program. Federally funded.

Togo steps up to jump in, but as he moves away from the statue, it starts to tip dangerously, threatening to fall. He catches it just in time. Duck shakes a scolding finger at him.

WANGA If you have any questions, you can call our supervisor Wendell at the office. He should be in first thing tomorrow.

Duck and Togo duct tape the base of the statue.

LIKO He would be in, but he's on jury duty this week, remember?

WANGA Oh yeah. Jury duty.

LIKO But you can talk to his assistant.

WANGA Joycelyn. That's her name. J-O-Y-C-E-lyn.

LIKO See? We get the job order from the department right here.

Liko flashes the clip board. We can see relief register on Liko and Wanga's faces.

WANGA Oh, no. No problem officer.

LIKO We totally understand. You just doing your job, we just doing ours.

WANGA Mahalo for stopping by. We'll tell Joycelyn to make sure to give you folks one heads-up call next time, yeah?

LIKO Yeah, sorry about that. City and County. You know how it is.

BOY Union benefits, but. Cannot go wrong!

The boys watch the unseen person walk away.

WANGA Damn, that was too fricken close.

TOGO. And you guys. So nervous you practically scream guilty. Man, you guys need some slaps.

LIKO At least I not the one when almost drop Duke Kahanamoku. That's so disrespectful.

TOGO No make me make you sorry you told the policeman to go away.

BOY Stop it already, you guys. Look. Brother Duke is facing the ocean.

WANGA Wow.

LIKO You guys take notice something different.

BOY Just like he smiling, yeah?

Our quiet actor playing the statue has a small smile on his face.

TOGO You guys crazy.

LIKO I know you see it too, Togo.

WANGA You see it, Duck? You see his face?

DUCK Fourteen joys and a will to be merry.

LIKO What?

DUCK It's Party time.

LIKO I don't know. I'm all pumped now. Let's go do something else.

TOGO Yeah, let's go Diamond Head and beat up those eco-tour guys. I hate those bastards.

DUCK Patience, grasshopper. You leave many footprints on the rice paper.

WANGA We gotta do something special to celebrate. This is like, MONU-MENTAL.

BOY Watch out. Togo going get you for that.

TOGO I going get you for that.

DUCK Let's see. We could go back to the dorm and chug some beer.

TOGO Sound good to me.

BOY Or, we could do something different.

WANGA Like?

BOY I don't know. Go back to the dorm and chug some beer.

WANGA That's more like it.

All five exit.

SCENE V

. . . .

Wanga enters, excited. He's carrying a newspaper.

WANGA Front page, you guys!

LIKO No ways.

WANGA I thought pretty much would have something about it, but I wasn't even thinking front page.

LIKO Front page, full color picture.

WANGA Yup! Front page.

TOGO You get two choices. Either read 'em out loud, pass around the paper or shut up and prepare to die.

BOY Eh, math major. That's three choices. No wait. That's four.

LIKO Listen. (reading from paper.) City officials are baffled —

TOGO Like that's news.

LIKO City officials are baffled by apparent unauthorized work done over the Labor Day holiday on the Duke Kahanamoku statue in Waikiki. The statue of Hawaii's Olympic medalist swimmer was found turned 180 degrees from its original position. City and County officials say they'll have to conduct an impact study to decide whether to leave the statue in its current position or turn it back around.

BOY So what, they wen talk about the smile?

LIKO A crowd gathered in front of the statue when rumors started circulating that a smile had appeared upon the statue's face in response to the move. Said one woman, "He look happy now that he can spock da ocean. As' how, das why."

BOY As' how, das why.

DUCK Ain't that the truth.

LIKO Waikiki Hotel Association members have drafted a letter calling for the State to appropriate funds to create a special blue ribbon task force to oversee restoration of the statue to its original placement.

TOGO That's it. They on my list.

BOY Who on your list?

TOGO All those Waikiki Wendells.

LIKO So that's a pretty good article, huh? See, Kaleo, your uncle Hoalike is a Modern Day Menehune.

BOY We just like the Old Days Menehune, except we not short.

WANGA There's one kinda' weird part, though.

TOGO No tell me Jeremy Harris trying fo' take credit. Yeah, I beautify his coastal zone management he no watch out.

WANGA Read the last part, Liko.

LIKO Witnesses claim to have seen a group of five young men wearing white jumpsuits hanging around the statue on Monday. One police officer who declined to give his name —

TOGO Even though it's embroidered onto his navy blue polyester shirt! Hello.

LIKO — said - quote — "I thought so they was the real deal. I mean, come on, they had a clip board."

WANGA Whoa, Liko.

LIKO You see! You see how it is?!

BOY You da man, Liko. You da clipboard man!

DUCK Don't forget, though. In Jun Ken Po, duct tape beat clip board every time.

WANGA Okay okay. Keep reading.

LIKO The outfits worn by the anonymous work crew had the letters SSS embroidered on the back.

BOY Samson Saumalu and Son House painting. Cannot go wrong!

LIKO Oh no. They made up their own interpretation. They calling us the Super Secret Squad.

There's silence as each tries to determine how to react. The guys all look at one another, trying to get a read on each other. Finally, Togo breaks the silence.

TOGO That name bites, man!

POEM FOR GEORGE HELM
ALOHA WEEK 1980

Eric Chock

I was in love with the word "aloha"
Even though I heard it over and over
I let the syllables ring in my ears
and I believed the king with outstretched hand
was welcoming everyone who wanted to live here
And I ignored the spear in his left hand
believing instead my fellow humans
and their love for these islands in the world
which allow us to rest from the currents
and moods of that vast ocean from which we all came
But George Helm's body is back in that ocean
I want to believe in the greatness of his spirit
that he still feels the meaning of that word
which is getting so hard to say

I thought there was hope for the word "aloha"
I believed when they said there are ways
in this modern technological world Oahu alone
could hold a million people
And we would become the Great Crossroads of the Pacific
if we used our native aloha spirit
our friendly wahines and our ancient hulas
They showed us our enormous potential
and we learned to love it
like a man who loves some thing in gold or silver
But these islands are made of lava and trees and sand
A man learns to swim with the ocean
and when he's tired he begins to search
for what he loves, for what will sustain him
George Helm is lost at sea
The bombing practice continues on Kahoolawe
I want to believe in what he was seeking
I want to believe that he is still swimming
toward that aina for which he feels
that word which is so hard to say

I want to believe in the word
But Brother George doesn't say it
He doesn't sing it in his smooth falsetto
in the melodies of aloha aina
There is no chance of seeing him walk up to the stage
pick up his guitar and smile the word at you across the room
The tourists, they twist their malihini tongues
The tour guides mouth it with smog-filled lungs
Politicians keep taking it out, dusting off the carcass
of a once-proud 3 syllable guaranteed vote-getter
You find its ghosts on dump trucks, magazines
airplanes, rent-a-cars
anywhere they want the dollar
They can sell you anything with aloha and a smile
even pineapples that came here from
(you guessed it) America!
They'll sell you too, servants of the USA
And if you don't believe they have the nerve
think of the ocean
They put up signs as close as they dare
And when his spirit comes back to land
the first thing he'll see is a big sign with that word
painted on, carved in, flashing with electricity
That word, so hard to say

I was going to believe that word
I was going to believe all those corporations
that seemed to spring up like mushrooms after a light rain
I was going to believe when they divided up
the home-land of a living people
and called it real estate or   50th state
or   Aloha State
I was going to believe we would still be able
to go up to the mountains, out to the country beaches
to the ocean where waves wash the islands
the islands which remind us we've all traveled a long way to get here

We all wanted a garden of our own in the world
We believed we'd all have peace
(and a piece of the aloha and of the state if we worked for it)
We're all pursuing the same dream!
So many of us are trying to get to the mountains, the beaches
so many trying to swim in the waves
legs kicking, arms paddling like the arms
of George Helm stroking towards a familiar beach
which he respected and belonged to by birth
for which he felt something no word can express
except for that word which is hard to say
unless we all live it!

I want to live the word "aloha"
But the body of George Helm is lost at sea
the practice continues on Kahoolawe
the buildings follow the roads
the roads carry thousands of cars filled with people
following their dreams of Hawaii or Paradise
to Waikiki where girls sell their hips
singers sell their voices
the island which has been sold is lit up all night
while the king with outstretched hand
has forgotten how to use his spear
George Helm is dead
and that word is not forgotten
It rings in my ears every day
I want us to live the word "aloha"
but it's so hard just to say

PONO

excerpt from *Hanai: A Poem for Queen Liliuokalani*
John Dominis Holt

To hear new voices rise above
the din of daily explosions—
in the halls of law, the market place.
Makaainana voices with fresh songs to sing
Speaking of new strengths
Mind and body strengths,
Strengthening the hope of change—new joys
in this tiresome regimen of want and confusion.
Grand queen sleep the ageless
sleep in peace
Your people rise now,
and demand their share
of this sweet and wondrous place.
The populace from their sleep of compliance
Awake now to the beat of new
drums hewn from betrayal and delusion
urging the makaainana voice to
rise above the din of daily
trumpetings of man and machine
To be rid of confusion and fear
To stand equally with the new
rulers of this precious place
to be ruthless in demanding what is ours.
To stand with you good Queen
To sing of life and joy
So put to rest the restless
ancients waiting on the
mountain tops and in their valley caves.
They will leave for their rest in far places
only when Hawai'i-iki once again
welcomes home its children
of the fisherman, the taro growers
the feather workers, the carver of
living gods, the canoe makers,
The house builders, growers of mamake and

ulu, the laborer and the stevedore
only when they are no longer denied
their share of this good land
and its riches.
You have given courage and hope good Queen
and today we sing new songs,
offer up strong prayers, and
look to revitalized creations of mind and spirit
careful to keep our innocence
unshackled and secure
for those to come when the
ghosts of our makua no longer
haunt the streets while others
fill us with confusion and
delusive hopes, with dreams of
twisted forms and obscure desires
which do not fuse us with new mana
created in the light of day,
born from the darkest
of Makahiki nights.
Queen Liliuokalani is gone
but she is here.
Reach out and touch her, she is here.
She might touch you
aloha mau e me ke moi wahine.
e Liliu lani e.
e Liliu lani e.
Amidst the crowded hum of highway sonority
In the tall blocks of mirrored concrete giants
On mountain tops, in green valleys
and all across the land
We sing new songs, create sharper visions
and we shout with pride
give us back what is left of what was ours
Our pride, our hopes.
And what about our lands?
They belong to us. Give them back.
We sleep no longer in compliance.
We have awakened with the beat

of ancient pahu,
the shark skin stretched tight,
and move determined to a new
rhythm, a new beat.
Aloha aina, aloha aina, E
Hawaii aloha e.

THE SOURCE
Imaikalani Kalahele

For Sam

from the source

    revolve   to the source

the secret must   for the source

for capable hands   the secret revolves

from capable hands   to capable hands

          revolve

          revolve

          revolve

THE BOY SLEPT UNDER THE BRIDGE
Matthew Kaopio

I stand on a sandy hill, and the salty air smells of geraniums and eucalyptus. I'm back at Grandma's house. I hear her banging around the kitchen and singing along to 1420 on the AM radio. I always loved being at Grandma's; it gave me such a strong sense of security. Safe. Sound. She calls my name. It's been some time since I've heard it. "'Īkau! 'Īkauikalani! Come eat, the food is ready. Hele mai, pā'ina!" I walk into the kitchen, where she's wiping the dishes at the sink. She still has her legs. I run up to her to give her a hug. She kisses me on the cheek and whispers in my ear, "Mariah Wong. Look for her, and remember."

The boy was jolted awake by a burning, stinging sensation on his left knee. With his eyes shut tightly, his blind fingers ran across a rapidly swelling mound of flesh with two small holes where the centipede had bit him. He jumped up and wildly searched through his things to see where it had gone. But with no sign of it, he settled back down and tried to resume his dream.

It had been weeks since his grandmother died, but sometimes he felt as if he were once again living with her on the farm in Kahalu'u. Along with his name, which he was ashamed of and never used, that time was gone and existed only in his memories. He was fourteen and had nowhere to go. His mother had left when he was seven, and his grandmother was his only family. Bills for dialysis and cancer treatments had run so high that the bank had foreclosed on their homestead. Without any income, they couldn't af-ford the rent in Honolulu. When she was hospitalized, most of their things were taken to the dump by the angry landlord. All that the boy owned in the world were a few clothes, his grandmother's quilt, and a braided lock of hair she gave him the night she died, which he kept tucked away in a pink Almond Roca tin can.

Eventually, he'd found a place to sleep under a bridge near the fishpond at Ala Moana Beach Park. It was dry, secluded, and safe. Although he had a centipede for a roommate, the soft grass formed a nest that cradled him as he lay under his grandmother's handmade quilt, and nobody bothered him.

He squinted at the sky. God was painting again. The boy admired the way the foamy, fizzy grape-soda clouds became streaked with strawberry sherbet. Lavender plumes turned into coral-rose flames, then juicy tangerine, and finally sweet lemonade. Every day, the sunrise was different, and each had its own story to tell. This morning, an orange dolphin cloud swam bliss-fully in a burgundy sea. From nowhere, a tangerine shark cloud billowed and began to attack. Just as the shark's teeth sank in, the dolphin swung around and jabbed its nose into the shark's side, shattering it into millions of canaries. The dolphin then devoured the birds one by one, the clouds merging. The boy knew this was a true sign that it would be a good day.

He loved dawn and dusk because those were the times that the sun was closest to the earth and that God listened to prayers and often responded. With reverence, the boy flung open his arms and embraced the morning, kissing the cheek of God. Then he got up.

He started his daily routine. Over his black T-shirt, he put on his denim jacket. Covered with original Hawaiian tattoo designs drawn with a permanent marker, it was his greatest work of art. Next, he dusted off his quilt, folded it diagonally, and tied the opposite corners into a knot, converting it into a pouch for his few possessions. He combed his tangled hair with his fingers and plucked out the leaves. Then he walked across the grass, noting that the beach park was not yet crowded with visitors. He marveled at the vividness of his dream. It was as if his grandmother was still alive, talking to him face-to-face. But it had been years since she could walk. Those days had been filled with trips to the beach to catch crabs, pick 'opihi, and harvest hā'uke'uke or to the mountains to catch prawns and gather Hawaiian herbs. When her diabetes worsened, she became confined to a wheelchair, and he became her legs. He had helped her the best he could. What puzzled him about the dream was the name, she uttered: Mariah Wong. And her telling him to remember. Remember what? he wondered. He was sure he'd never heard the name before. Was Grandma sending him a message from the other side?

The early-morning air tasted delicious on his tongue, and he drank the sweet tonic without wasting one drop. He was so hungry he could have eaten a rubber slipper. He entered the restroom to get cleaned up and found it deserted. Keeping his torn surf shorts on, he stepped into the shower and shocked his nerves with a cold-water blast. Hi'uwai, he remembered. That's what Grandma called the first morning cleansing. Normally done either in the ocean or in a mountain pond, it gave one the chance to spiritually, as well as physically, wash away the debris of the previous day to begin the new day fresh.

The boy loved being clean. Despite what others thought, so did most of the other beach people. Spying a small hotel shampoo bottle on the shower floor, he opened it and lathered his body with the pearly liquid. Soon he was covered from head to toe in rich, perfumed lather.

He closed his eyes and let the water pummel his face. He imagined he was again standing under the mountain waterfall where his grandmother took him to catch prawns. They'd gather pepeiao, bamboo shoots, fern shoots, green papayas, and wild sweet-potato leaves, and she would cook up her famous jungle stew.

Grandma often let him swim before returning home, and once, while standing under he rushing waterfall, he'd felt as if he were undergoing a kind of baptism. Though the water was icy cold, a warm sensation had entered the top of his head and spread throughout his body, and he had imagined that his entire being had been touched by the finger of God. Now, for just a moment, it almost felt as if he was standing under that waterfall again. But then he heard voices echoing by the urinals, and the reverie ended.

He shut the shower off and dried his body with a towel he'd smuggled out of his grandmother's hospital room. He changed into his only pair of jeans, worn out around the knees, and put on his last clean T-shirt. He washed his dirty clothes in the sink with more of the shampoo and squeezed out the water. He slung his pouch over his shoulder and gathered up his wet laundry, then looked at himself in the mirror. Framing a slim, golden-skinned face were knotted, sun-bleached dreadlocks that fell to his shoulders. His thin nose and green eyes had been inherited from an unknown Caucasian father, probably some military transient his mother had brought home one night. Most boys his age suffered from acne, but his face was smooth. Bronze fuzz sprouted around his lips. He wasn't bad looking, and even though he was part Hawaiian, for years other children had called him "stupid haole."

He was used to harassment. In the park, people ogled his nappy hair or judged him by the images drawn on his jacket. He accepted their treatment as an ugly part of life.

He emerged from the bathroom so hungry that he felt his stomach was eating itself. He draped his wet laundry on a tree to dry, then stretched his body out in the shade below. Opening his pouch, he rattled the Almond Roca can and counted the few coins he had stashed inside.

If he only had ten cents more, he could buy a refillable cup of coffee. And for another thirty-five cents, he could buy a day-old poppy-seed bagel and have a decent meal. Instead, he had to settle for stale chips and a piece of garlic chicken from a plate lunch he found in the trash. He leaned against the tree and took a swig from his water bottle.

And then there were the homeless. Some were professionals: white-color workers who were down on their luck and in desperate need of a temporary place to stay. Most were welfare recipients who'd been kicked out of low-income housing or ‘A‘ala Park. Others were teenage runaways, ex-cons, drug abusers, drunks, and people suffering from mental illness—all were scary looking, but most were harmless.

The old Chinese man was on the beach again, doing his morning exercises. The boy found the fluid movements mesmerizing. The man formed a small imaginary ball with his hands and pushed it away with a graceful sweep to his right; then he formed another imaginary ball and brushed it to his left. Next, he swept both arms outward as if swimming. On the park bench where she usually sat was the lady who fed the scavenger birds that dirtied the park with their droppings. The lady cackled and danced as if conducting an orchestra. Bobbing their heads before her were small turtledoves and larger, mostly white pigeons with bright, stop-sign-red beaks and feet. There were also fat lace-necked doves, brown mynahs with yellow beaks and eyes, red-breasted cardinals, and plenty of little brown and green birds that moved in waves like schools of fish, following the seeds that the lady sprinkled about.

Nearby, under a banyan tree, a red-eyed Asian woman was trying to wake her invisible friend and getting annoyed. The boy had seen her arguing with the air many times. Once when he'd politely said hello, she'd scolded her friend for not returning the greeting.

The boy often felt invisible himself: he would try to melt into his surroundings like a chameleon and observe the tourists who swarmed the park. Some of the Japanese had skin so pale and translucent that it almost appeared blue, and they shielded its delicacy from the sun by all means possible. Others applied liberal amounts of cocoa butter to their brown outer husks. Some of the young Japanese kids had bleached-blond hair, red spikes, or anime superhero-style wisps of pink and purple clumps. One young man with long, fake dreadlocks like a Rastafarian's would have passed for a light-skinned Jamaican if it weren't for his Japanese accent. "Bafaro soruja, borun in Amerika," he sang as he listened to a Bob Marley tune.

And then the boy noticed a man struggling to slip a dollar bill into one of the vending machines.

Sitting in a mechanized wheelchair, the man was small, in his midforties maybe, and had salt-and-pepper hair, a basketball-sized stomach, and two shriveled legs, which hung limply. His hands were so gnarled that he resembled a sea lion clapping his flippers together. The boy impulsively went over to him.

"You need help?" he asked.

"Thanks, brah!" the man said with a smile. The boy took the dollar.

"What's your name, cuz?" the man asked.

"Me?" The boy thought about the dream in which his grandmother said his name and how good it had felt. He swallowed hard. "'Īkau," he said softly. "I'm 'Īkau."

"Right on, Brudah E! I'm Alex. Make a fist." The boy did, and the man tapped his hooked hand against it, saying loudly, "Bam!"

"Bam!" repeated the boy, grinning. He fed the dollar bill into the machine. "Which button should I press?"

"I like dah chips! Press A-4."

"Okay, it's fifty-five cents."

The boy pressed A and 4. The chips fell with a soft thud, and the change dropped into the coin-return slot with three loud chi-chings.

"You can grab 'em for me, cuz?" asked the man. The boy fetched the chips and scooped out the coins. "Here's your change," he said.

"Nah, brah, keep 'em."

Again, the man held out his hooked hand. The boy made a fist and they bammed each other before the man rode away, tearing his bag of chips open with his teeth. The boy gazed at the coins in his hand as if they were stars that had fallen from the sky.

He gathered the rest of his money, approached the fast-food counter, and bought the last day-old bagel and a cup of coffee. He ate ravenously. Because the coffee was refillable, he went back several times. Each cup was topped with loads of sugar and powdered cream. It was the best meal he had eaten in a long time.

DESECRATION: THE BONE OF MY CONTENTION
Kekuewa Kikiloi

A simple lesson:
Of how you damage my present day
    manifestation
Claimin I have no direct relation
Interested only in science & human creation
Lacking ETHICS in the soul of your occupation
You see… here is the bone of my contention…

When?
When will you stop the digging of ancestral
    graves?
Leaving it exposed… harmed by penetrating
    rays…

When?
When will you stop and realize?
The hurt that runs deep in my peepos cries…

When?
When will you begin to understand?
I am the spiritual today, but the physical must
be returned to the land

When?
When will you stop the bullshet and madness?
And start to think of the implications of your
    actions…

So I will repatriate and rebury YOUR mistakes
Help your narrow mind equate
that the next time you measure a bone you find
whether u can conceive this in your simple
    mind
it doesn't come from the skeleton of a past time
rather it is being ripped from the emBODYment
    of mine.

UA AO HAWAIʻI

Larry Kauanoe Lindsey Kimura

Kau e ka wena o ke ao i ka lani
He wekeweke i ka pō pili puka
He ʻelele o ka poniponi hikina
Kau ke kāheʻa wanaʻao i ka ʻāla ʻapapa
Laʻi ana i luna o ke kūkulu o ka lani lā
ʻO kaʻu ia e huli alo nei i ka ulu ē
ʻAe, ʻae, ua ao ē, ē, ē, ē, ē.

Hō mai lā ko mālamalama
I ka honua nei i ka mauli ola
Ua ao Hawaiʻi ke ʻōlino nei
Mai ka piʻina a ka welona a ka lā
Kāhiko ʻia i ka ʻike manomano
Ka ʻike kōliʻu mai o kikilo mai
ʻO kaʻu nō ia ʻo ka pūlama
A paʻa ma ka ipu o ka ʻike ē.
ʻAe, ʻae, ua ao ē, ē, ē, ē, ē.

He mele no Hawaiʻi, ua ao.

The announcement of dawn appears as a glowing streak upon the heavens
It is a narrow opening in the darkness heralding the day
It is a messenger of the purple glimmer from the east
Streaks of red color appear in the long cloud formations
Reposing serenely upon the pillars holding up the heavens
I turn to gaze and focus now on the growth and the rising of a new day
Yes, yes, it is now dawn.

O grant to us your radiant light
Here upon the earth, to stir us with the spirit of life
Hawaiʻi is in the brightness of day, it shines brilliant
From its boundaries from the east to the west
It wears as its finery a myriad of knowledge
Of deep insight from the depths of antiquity
My sole duty is to embrace and to cherish
So it may be firm in the repositories of enlightenment
Yes, yes, here now is the brightness of day.

A mele in honor of Hawaiʻi in a new dawn.

INTENTION AND ITS ROLE IN KNOWING SOMETHING
excerpt from
The Role of History, Intention, and Function: More Thoughts on Hawaiian
Epistemology
Manu Aluli Meyer

> Ke hoʻi aʻela ka ʻōpua i Awalau
> The rain clouds are returning to Awalau
> Said of a return to the source

The origin of thought, even before sound begins to shape language, is found
in intention. This is why it was hewa to even think of slapping a child's
head—the first piko that connects us to our kūpuna. The thought was said
to have been punishable with consequences seen and unseen. Here is where
history sits down to chat with mind. Given the nature of protocol, or the ritu-
als for how one enters the ocean and forest, or even our neighbor's yard, is it
any wonder that Hawaiians have something to say about intention?

Intention is the portal to right action, it inspires motivation, movement,
and why we understand anything. We must first watch our intention, then
prepare, then set out into excellence. How can this happen in classrooms set
up to create uniform thinkers? A distinctly empowered identity is simply
impossibility in this scenario and the creative mind, the awakened child, or
the cultural adolescent will naturally question, and sometimes resist, what is
considered mainstream. *This is a good thing.* Current research that links Hawaiian cultural alignment with poor educational achievement highlights this
tension. There is *always* more than meets the eye in research, especially with
regard to what exactly is appropriate understanding of Hawaiian culture.

How do we know our youth exhibit or practice the true depth of what it
means to be courageous, and are they shaped by aloha? Or do they just exist
as cartoon caricatures on the back of "KOA WARRIOR" t-shirts? I believe
that many of our children *do not* have a true grounding in nā mea waiwai
and thus resist mainstream norms because their idea of "culture" demands
it of them. Hawaiian culture does exist in this scenario; it is simply not the
culture that has birthed itself around thirty-six aliʻi at Kūkaniloko. Inherent
in this discussion of the correlation with culture and poor SAT scores is the
assumption that our current system is the ideal and that students who do not
aspire to that goal are "at risk." Surely, someone can stand up to that weakest
of arguments: "If you're not like us, then you are deficient."

We are more than the sum of our empirical parts and liabilities and more than the average of someone else's norm, and we are certainly more than our incomes. We are Hawaiians living in colonized islands, in breathtaking beauty in the center of the Pacific Ocean and it is our intention that links us to a wider menu of knowledge opportunities and intellectual pursuits. Of course, intentions are inspired by history, culture and the needs of those around us. We know that knowledge is responsibility so why give us only information or the promise of minimum wage work? Understanding intention deepens the dialogue we can have with schools as they become places for practice, moral development, and cultural extension.

We did not teach children who did not want to learn. Maria Montessori and John Dewey would applaud our sensibility here. We understood that energy was perfect if we did not muddy its intention. What is the child interested in? How do we match their interest with the needs of our society? What does it really mean to educate someone? Here is the fine line intention leads us to walk on. What do we really wish for our children? What is the intention of our lives and how will we best thrive?

We have let others answer those questions for us. This is why history is a dynamic tool—a tool that is now being shaped by our own minds. Soon, our "new" history, the history we write will alter my reality, change my faith and allow me to re-enter my own sense of self-efficacy. I will see that a Hawaiian idea of intelligence is a fullness that modernity struggles with, a round and rich expression of place and people that is old and new as winter is both hot and cold. Soon I will experience knowledge as something I create, a balance between mind and body, history and this present moment. It will be my intention that slices through mediocre epistemological expectations and serves up a more life-sustaining example of what happens when all of my mana, my shadow exists inside of me—a moment when I am truly akamai. We will all be a part of re-defining what intelligence is because we will know more of what it was. We will know, we will know.

CAN YOU KEEP A SECRET?

Mary Kawena Pukui and Caroline Curtis

Poko was fishing with Grandfather. They had come out at dawn, and the boy had watched the daylight grow. Ocean and sky were pink like a pearl shell, all but one low gray cloud — a low gray cloud that rested on the waves.

They paddled toward the cloud, and it rose slowly, uncovering an island. The island was more green and beautiful than anything the boy had ever seen, and it was filled with growing things. Tall cocopalms were heavy with ripe nuts, bananas shone like the sun itself, plants, vines, and trees were large and very green. Suddenly a cock crowed, and the cloud settled down once more upon the island.

"Grandfather!" the boy whispered. "What is that land? Let us go there!"

"It is one of the hidden islands of Kane, and we cannot go to it."

"Why not, Grandfather? Didn't you see how green and beautiful it is? I want to go there. I want to see it all. Come, Grandfather, let us go."

"Grandson," the old man answered solemnly, "this I have heard: If the gods move that land close to the homes of men, then one can reach it in an hour. But often the land is hidden, and one may sail the ocean until he is gray-headed and never find it. Today the gods gave us sight of that fair land, and then they hid it. It is gone from us forever." The boy said no more, but his heart was filled with longing.

Poko became a man, married, and had a fine family whom he loved. Still, the thought of that beautiful green island stayed with him. Still he longed to go there.

Today he and his family were in Puna visiting relatives. His wife and her cousins talked together of kapa-making and other women's matters. Tired of listening, Poko wandered off along the beach. He found a shady spot and sat down to rest. He leaned against a rock and dreamily watched a log rolling in the surf. Up the beach it came, pushed by the waves, then down again. As he watched, Poko thought again of the hidden island. If only he might go there! Perhaps he slept.

Suddenly he was roused by a hand upon his shoulder. He sprang up and looked into the face of a woman he had never seen before. Her *pa-'u* was of dark seaweed, her lei and bracelets were of shells. "You dream of the hidden island of Kane," she said, and her voice was like the song of pebbles washed by the waves. "I am the daughter of Kane. I will take you to that hidden land. Come with me."

The young man followed the stranger down the beach. He saw her touch the rolling log. It became a canoe, and they stepped in. The woman paddled.

The canoe slipped through the waves as swiftly as a fish and as quietly. Poko's heart was full of joy. He did not know whether they paddled a short distance or far when, just ahead, he saw the low-lying cloud. It lifted, and underneath he saw the good green land he had seen long ago.

The canoe scraped on the beach. The two jumped out, carried the canoe up on the sand and looked about them. It was as the young man remembered only more beautiful. Strange trees dropped ripe fruit. Strange birds sang. Here was a garden where sugarcane reached far above his head. Sweet potatoes burst from the rich earth. Ripe bananas and breadfruit dropped from plant and tree. A fat pig waddled through the garden, so well fed it only sniffed the fruit. A fat dog lay sleeping in the sun. Farther on, he saw a hen sitting on eggs among the grasses. Another called softly to her chicks. It was a home-like land—only there were no people and no homes.

The young man turned to the woman who still walked at his side. "I want to stay!" he said. "Oh, let me live here always!"

"You may stay," she answered.

Suddenly, with the eyes of his mind, Poko saw his wife. He saw the white flowers about her head, her hand resting lovingly on the fat baby. And he saw his girl and boy. Turning to the daughter of Kane he said, "I cannot stay alone. I want my wife and children."

"Can you keep a secret?" the woman asked.

The young man looked at her in wonder. "Yes," he answered.

"Then you and your family may live here all your lives."

The two launched the canoe and paddled back to Puna. As they stepped out, their canoe became once more a log rolled by the waves.

The daughter of Kane spoke earnestly to Poko. "Keep your secret well. Do not tell anyone where you have been. Do not tell anyone where you are going. When six days have passed bring your family to this beach. If you have kept your secret I will come for you, and you shall live upon the hidden island." Then she was gone.

The young man hurried home in great excitement. His wife saw his excitement and his joy. "What has happened?" she asked.

He smiled "I cannot tell you," he answered. "In six days go with me to the beach, you and the children. Then you shall know."

Others were about. There was talk and laughter, and the wife said no more, but that night when they were alone she asked again. "I cannot tell," he repeated.

"If you love me you must tell," she begged.

He tried to put her off, but still she begged. At last he asked her, "Can you keep a secret?"

She looked at him surprised and answered, "Yes, I can."

Then he told her, "Today I visited the hidden land of Kane. Six days must pass. Then we can all go there to live — you and the children and I. Only remember: No one must know. We must keep the secret." They talked long that night. He told her of the beauty of that land, of its fruit and vegetables, its pigs and chickens. They were so excited they could hardly sleep.

Next morning the children noticed the excitement and the joy. "What is it, Mother?" they asked. "What is going to happen?"

"I cannot tell," the mother answered. "It is a secret. When six days have passed your father will take us all to the beach over there. Then you will know."

"We want to know now!"

"What is it, Mother? We can keep a secret."

At last she told. "Remember," she whispered, "no one must know."

Six days is a long time to wait. The little daughter whispered to her friend, "Can you keep a secret?" Then she told her that the whole family were going to do what no family had ever done. The daughter of Kane would take them to a hidden land.

"Can you keep a secret?" the boy asked the friend who surfed with him. "We are going to an island where is the best surfing in the world," and he too told.

The day came. Before the sun had risen father, mother and children had reached the beach. But they were not alone! The news had spread. Quietly the neighbors gathered. All the village had come to see them off.

There was the log rolling up the beach and down, washed by the waves, but the daughter of Kane did not come. The log did not change to a canoe. Poko looked longingly over the ocean. "I did not keep the secret," he said sadly.

His wife picked up her baby and looked about happily at her friends. "I think we should have been very lonely in that hidden land," she whispered.

Told to Mary Kawena Pukui by an old man whose mother came from Puna.

'ANAKALA KALĀHELE'S LOVE-HATE LECTURE

Sage U'ilani Takehiro

In dis worl', only can Love or Hate. Cuz all get in between is frustration and jealousy. And dat, no can. Sometimes you trip out, you trip out, you trip out some moa—nex ting you know you tripping all ova da place until sometin pull on da Love line—Boom, you fall down, den pau. Stan up feeling like one champ all smiles and Nobody, not No-damn-fricken-body, can tax your mana because you—Because You—get da powa, fo' geeev 'um! Keep 'um, eat 'um, do what feel good to you man, do whatevah feel goood to you.

Sometimes, some individuals, dey gotta Hate. Dey no can help. Like when da wahine get dea da kine, dea ma'i ah, Hooo—Watch Out! Dea homones li'dat stay getting all nuts. Dey trip out, dey trip out, dey trip out some moa cuz dey gotta go work, dey gotta do dis, dey gotta do dat. But for real kine brah all dey like do is lay down an eat chocolate Hagendaz. Nah, no need be Hagendaz but gotta be chocolate brah. Gotta be chocolate, cuz chocolate tastes like looove. An when da wahine stay trippin', gotta geeve 'um Love—Even if she ready fo' buss yo' eye cuz you tol' her neva have chocolate . . . "But no worry, no worry Bebe, get Rocky Ro-oad" . . . Ok, she pau be piss off, grab da spoon, scoop da mashmello, melt 'um on her toungue. Den oooh, she Looove you—until she bite into one nut, den ho man she get all nuts . . . "My teet soah, my back soah, my whole body soah—You No Undastan!" . . . "No Bebe, I dunno whatchu talkin' about. But I Looove you!"

Sometimes, some people, dey jus hate cuzzz—Ahh Dunno? Dey get problems as why. But everybody get problems and da ting not going kill you—If you Love 'um. But if you hate 'um den sorry brah, you dead. But if you Love death den death going Love you back but you not going be dead. And if you hate death then death going hate you back and you going be dead brah, you going be dead, pau, no can. Hate is stale. Hate is stink. Hate is souah. Hate is Uuugly, brah. Hate is Uuugly. Hate is hamajang.

In dis worl', everybody Love. Sometimes individuals trip out, dey get frustrated, dey get jealous a da people who feel no hamajang like dem—Anden, Boom!—Sometimes, in dis worl', everybody Hate. But imagine one stale worl' all stink, all souah, all Uuugly—no can. Da pilikia going come brah, da pilikia going come, trip you out, trip you out, try tax your mana, try kill you.

But you get da powa Braddah, Sista, Cuz, you get da powa fo' breathe, fo' keep da 'ea circulating so no come stale, no come stink, no come souah. So mo' bettah Love den Hate brah, mo bettah love den hate—you know why? Cuz can.

I GEDDUM

D. Ululani Uchima

You know wen sometin on yo mind, an you no can shake um, yo whole day kine-a bummed, yeah? Well, one time I was driving up da road, an da cah in fronna me wen stop at da red light. On top da cah's bumpa had one old sticka wit da words EDDIE WOULD GO. Ho, I wen trip out! Neva make sense. I wen tink, so wat? Wazzat about? Dey come out wit dum kine stickas nowdays. I no geddum!

Afta dat, ereytime I wen see dat kine bumpa sticka on one cah, I look at who stay drivin fo see wat kine guy goin put one sticka laddat on his cah. Ho, was anykine guys! Ole kine. Young keeds. Mosely local guys but. Dis bumpa sticka wen really bodda me. I no was mad laddat, but da words jus wen stuck in my mind all da time. So fo litto while I wen read ereybody's bumpa sticka, cuz maybe get mo stuffs I suppose to know. I figga bumpa stickas, dey jus like newspaypaz.

I no buy da paypa steady, kay, cuz wasse money. Get too much crap goin on in da world today. Who like pay good money fo read crap? Not me, man. But da odda day, I wen pick up somebody else's newspaypa, an I wen read by da sports page about deese canoe guys. Ho, my eyes wen almose pop out wen I read about dis guy Eddie. He was one good swimma an one good surfa. He wen really know da ocean laddat. Eddie no sked da wadda. I wen tink, eh, dis da same Eddie on da bumpa sticka or wat? Ho, long time I wen geeve up readin bumpa stickas arready. One time I almose rap da guy in fronna me. I wen come too close so dat I could read dem stickas. Too many chances I wen take. Nowdays get planny sue jobs, you know.

Den one time wen I stay drivin work, I hea da raedjo disc jockeys on da Hawaiian station talkin story about wat wen happen ousside da sea. I neva hea ereytin dat dey was talkin about, but I did hea da part about how deese guys wen get stranded on one canoe an how dey wen need help. So one guy on da canoe, dat guy Eddie, ho, he was so sharp man. He wen tell dem guys on da canoe fo no worry. He geddum. Eddie wen dive insai da wadda an, poom, he wen swim out! He gutsy, yeah? But da disc jockey guys, dey wen say dat all da canoe guys wen get saved, but not Eddie. He neva even reach da shore. Had one big search fo him, but dey neva wen find him. He wen love da sea so much, da sea wen take him. Jus laddat! Eveybody tink dat maybe now he stay wit his surfboard buddies in da sky. Ho, wat wen stuck in my mind was da guy who wen call in fo talk on da raedjo. He wen say dat out of all da guys on da canoe, Eddie was da one who would jump out of da canoe jus fo chrai save his friends. "Eddie would go!"

Ho, I stay cryin now jus tinkin about wat dat guy on da raedjo wen say about Eddie. An you know dat sticka I wen see long time before? Now I geddum.

The Voices of the Future

KAONA

KAONA

Jamaica Osorio and Ittai Wong

Ua ola ka olelo mai ka paiku ana o na pua
Our language survived through the passing of flowers.
In 1896, the last reigning monarch of Hawaii, Queen Liliuokalani,
was held prisoner in her own palace.
Communication with the outside world was prohibited,
thus newspapers were snuck into her room wrapped
around flowers.

For months our Queen and her people
wrote songs and stories hidden in Hawaiian,
so as to converse without
the Overthrowing Provisional Government knowing.
It is because of this we know our history
the language of Hidden meanings

Kaona
the first written Hawaiian poetry;
songs and dance were the medium
in which we decoded their denotation
connecting connotation through Kaona
speaking of flowers, but meaning children
Ua maikai ke kalo i ka oha
The branch is a reflection of the taro root

We are a reflection of our genesis
The most intricate euphemisms that ever existed.

You had to understand the history and culture
to decrypt this language. Had to dig deeper than dictionaries
beneath esophagus
and vocal cords
to grasp the root of the words our people would chant
just to understand their messages

This is kaona
in a time where our freedom of speech was denied
and words needed to be hidden in order to be heard.
The language of commonality was no longer an option,
so our oral traditions evolved else words would die.

Our language survived through the passing of flowers	Ua ola ka olelo mai ka paiku ana o na pua
Our ancestors survived through the passing of tongues	Ua ola na iwi mai ka paiku ana o ka olelo
A dying language wrapped a dying culture	Ua owili ia ka makou keiki me ka olelo
Our flowers	Na Pua
Our Children	Na Pua
The ones we promised to die for weren't surviving	Ke moe i ka make nei ka makou mau keiki
So we sent our stories	No laila ua paiku makou na moolelo
Wrapped our children in blankets of words	Wahii na keiki me na kapa o na olelo
Hoping they hold on to their meanings	manaolana makou e paa ana lakou i na manao

E ho mai ka ike mai luna mai e
O na mea huna noeau
O na mele
E ho mai
E ho mai
E ho mai e

So today I pray
for the winds to blow understanding to her
people upon the backs of change
I pray
that forgotten stories everywhere flood
through like the white washed ships,

which stripped our language away.
I pray
for every foreign tongue
to relearn its native kiss in language
formed as flowers,
spread across the lands we know as our own
hold the salvation of our souls through
the wishes begot long ago

Because some meanings should never be hidden
and with every word lost,
we lose a piece of ourselves
with every story forgot,
we lose a piece of our history
It's time to uncover the past that we may
understand our future
Interpret our stories that we may better know ourselves

E ho mai ka ike mai
luna mai e

O na mea huna noeau

O na mele

E ho mai

E ho mai

E ho mai e

E ho mai ka ike mai
luna mai e

O na mea huna noeau

O na mele

E ho mai

E ho mai

E ho mai e

So listen to me
    So listen to me
        So listen to me
           So listen to me
Listen to me.
Existence persists as long as we have language
if we cannot communicate with each other, we cannot survive.

He mana ko ka leo, a ina aohe leo aohe ola
without language, we have nothing
We must see to it that our language survives like the past,
through flowers Ua ola ka olelo mai ka paiku ana o na pua
E hiki na pua e ola mai ka paiku ana o ka olelo
so our children can survive, through the passing of language.

Questions for Discussion
and Writing

QUESTIONS FOR DISCUSSION AND WRITING

> For classroom use, a teacher's guide with discussion questions and writing prompts is available as a free PDF download at **www.hawaii.edu/crdg.**

Whether you are discussing the themes found in this book with friends, using them to initiate a class discussion, or finding inspiration for your own writing, there are a number of questions that can get you started thinking about any one of the selections or about the collection as a whole. What do the works in this anthology suggest about our relationships in terms of place, survival, and lifestyle? What are some factors that influence how we perceive concepts of time and the cultural indicators of time and place? How do the authors juxtapose social networks, such as family, with individuality? How do the different characters and their points of view compare, and what does this imply about our society? What ironies are evident in these works? What factors influence individual identity and identification? What are some of the struggles these works express? What is the significance of the authors' word and language choices? What is the significance of translation, and how does translation affect the original works and our interpretations of them?

When you read this anthology, think of the voices being carried by the collective works, beginning with "The Kumulipo" and closing with "Kaona." Throughout our lives, we all contribute to the balanced flow of the universe. This is Pono. Your place in the universe begins with kulāiwi—where you are and what you come from. Navigation is impossible to implement individually as many factors contribute to navigation. These contributing factors are 'ohana—the network of elements working together, as the vital organs and elements in our bodies function to give us life. Each function has an identity, each identity bonds to create a larger life form in the universe. Aloha kekahi i kekahi, love one another.

KEKAHI

One, someone, anyone. Do the voices in this section refer to one individual? Are there exchanges occurring between individual entities? What do the terms "here" and "there" mean? "Us" and "them?" How are individuals defined? How do they interact? Change? Develop? Stay the same? Kahi also refers to time. Jon Osorio's "I Come to the Water" reflects time and change, like water currents moving in our universe. How does "Pua Mana Nō" demonstrate the movement of time and space with imagery of modernization? What do other works in this anthology, such as Keola Beamer's "The Shimmering – Ka ʻOlili" and Holo Hoʻopai's "Culture Blind," imply about forms of identity and the shifts and exchanges from one form to another?

ʻOHANA

Relationships between individuals form ʻohana, a family, a network. How is this network symbolized in Caroline Curtis' "Nawai The Net Maker," Lisa Linn Kanae's "Lei Maker," and Imaikalani Kalahele's "Make Rope?" Does the idea of "making" support the idea of ʻohana having a function, a purpose, a continuous creation? How do kuʻualoha hoʻomanawanui's "Hoʻokupu," Adam Campbell's "Thirty Calibre," and Temujene Makua's "Love is All We Need" exemplify forms of ʻohana in relation to individuals? ʻOhana can refer to our biological families, our adopted families, or the surrounding environments that contribute to the creation of our individual identities. Jasmine Tua's "They Called Him Mango Man" and Olga Kalei Kalama's "Kuʻu Wā Liʻi Liʻi I Lāʻie" all evoke a sense of home. How do elements in the other works in this section create a sense of home? How is ʻohana created by relationships that connect individuals through time and space?

KULĀIWI

Kula may refer to a source, container, or field. Iwi is bone. Kulāiwi is an individual's or an ʻohana's native place, their home. The pieces in this section speak to the idea of home, the place where an individual is, the place where they come from, and perhaps the place where they end up. How do the characters in works such as Marjorie Sinclair's "Lava Watch" and Leialoha Apo Perkins' "The Beach at Napali" demonstrate the nature of movement?

How does "He Mele He'e Nalu (A Surfing Song)" exemplify relationships between individuals in a shared space? How do these examples demonstrate the role of place in the stories of our lives? How do Rene Sylva's "Native Plants," Danielle Ka'iulani Kauihou's "Ka I'a," and Makia Malo's "Lo'i Kalo" describe elements that characterize kulāiwi? How do "He Huaka'i Ka'apuni ma Hawai'i (Ramble Round Hawai'i)" and Keith Kalani Akana's "Press Down" speak to the movement of universal elements functioning together to create something larger than themselves?

PONO

Goodness, uprightness, morality, well-being, prosperity, just, virtuous—the name of this section has many implications. What do the works included in this section imply? Most works, like Mary Beth Aldosa's " 'Au 'A 'Ia" and excerpts from Lee Cataluna's "Super Secret Squad," imply challenges to the prosperity of Hawaiian values. What are these challenges? What challenges are addressed in Manu Meyer's "Intention and its Role in Knowing Something?" How are they different from those described by Aldosa and Cataluna? How does she invite us to understand the relationships between our individual selves, our 'ohana, and our kulāiwi? What do works such as D. Ululani Uchima's "I Geddum" teach us about taking responsibility for our own knowledge and learning? This section speaks to cultural, economic, and identity politics, but the section title may also refer to spiritual politics. How does Eric Chock's "Poem for George Helm" explore the power of words? How does John Dominis Holt's poem "Pono" explore the power of consciousness?

KAONA

"Kaona" was composed as a performance poem by Jamaica Osorio and Ittai Wong, two young poets who embody the future of Hawai'i. This poem has been performed in Hawai'i and in Washington, DC by Osorio, Wong, and their Youth Speaks Hawai'i teammates, Alakai Kotrys and Will Giles, who stand in response with the chant "E Ho Mai," while the poets weave their voices with dualities of language. "Kaona" is an exchange of meaning, an exchange between voices, dimension, space, and time. How does "Kaona" exemplify the prosperity of life across Hawaiian generations? How do you think your impression as a reader might differ from that of someone who encountered this poem as spoken word? How does the form of presentation affect the literature's power? How do voices carry the future? Are the voices of the future carried in multiple meanings, multiple dimensions?

Like a lei, this anthology opens with a preparation and greeting followed by acknowledgment of the creation, the Kumulipo. The first section of this book begins the process of picking individual flowers that we have gathered and organized. The second and third sections of this anthology string the collection together. Then, we close as a lei maker ties the end of a lei to its beginning. We offer this lei so the voices of Hawai'i will continue to carry us into the future.

The Curriculum Research & Development Group has made every effort to trace the ownership of all selections in this book and to make full acknowledgment and compensation for their use. For selections whose authors we could not find, the copyright remains with the owner of the work. We thank those who have granted us permission to reprint. This list follows the order in which selections appear in this book.

Kalahele, Imaikalani. "Hoʻomākaukau" from *Poetry and Art*. 2002. Honolulu: Kalamakū Press. Reprinted by permission of the author.

Liliuokalani of Hawaii, trans. Excerpt from *The Kumulipo: An Hawaiian Creation Myth*. 1978. San Francisco: Pueo Press.

Balaz, Joseph P. "Moeʻuhane" from *After the Drought*. 1985. Honolulu: Topgallant Publishing Co., Ltd. Reprinted by permission of the author.

Beamer, Keola. "Island Born" from *Jack de Mello Presents Keola & Kapono Beamer: Hawaii Then and Now*. 2001. Honolulu: Music of Polynesia. Reprinted by permission of the author.

Beamer, Keola. "The Shimmering – ka ʻolili" from *The Shimmering – ka ʻolili: Island Stories*. 2002. Lahaina, HI: ʻOhe Books. Reprinted by permission of the author.

Brooks, Kahi. "Hoʻi Hou i ka Mole" from *Huli Au ʻŌiwi 3, A Native Hawaiian Journal*. 2003. Honolulu: Kuleana ʻŌiwi Press. Reprinted by permission of the author.

Hamasaki, Richard. "Open It!" from *Spider Bone Diaries*. 2001. Honolulu: University of Hawai'i Press. Reprinted by permission of University of Hawai'i Press.

Ho'omanawanui, John Noah P. "Ke Ala 'Ili'ili o Hāloa" from *Huli Au 'Ōiwi 3, A Native Hawaiian Journal*. 2003. Honolulu: Kuleana 'Ōiwi Press. Reprinted by permission of the author.

Ho'opai, Holo. "Culture Blind" from *Write On, HEA!* 2001. Honolulu: Hawaii Education Association. Reprinted by permission of the author.

Kahanu, Hina. "Kahakai" from *Bamboo Ridge #84: The 25ᵗʰ Anniversary Issue*. 2003. Honolulu: Bamboo Ridge Press. Reprinted by permission of the author.

Kanae, Lisa Linn. 1999. "Island Girl" from *Look My Daughta and Other Poems and Prose: A Thesis Submitted to the Graduate Division of the University of Hawai'i in Partial Fulfillment of the Requirements for the Degree of Master of Arts in English*. May 2002. Honolulu. Reprinted by permission of the author.

Wong, Kealoha. "Lesson of Essence (Recess II)" from *Bamboo Ridge #84: The 25ᵗʰ Anniversary Issue*. 2003. Honolulu: Bamboo Ridge Press. Reprinted by permission of the author.

Osorio, Jonathan Kamakawiwo'ole. "I Come to the Water" from *Huli Au 'Ōiwi 3, A Native Hawaiian Journal*. 2003. Honolulu: Kuleana 'Ōiwi Press. Reprinted by permission of the author.

Pukui, Mary Kawena. "Pua Mana Nō (Sure a Poor Man)" from *The Echo of Our Song: Chants and Poems of the Hawaiians*. Mary Kawena Pukui and Alfons L. Korn, eds. & trans. 1973. Honolulu: The University Press of Hawaii. Reprinted by permission of University of Hawai'i Press.

Campbell, Adam. "Thirty Calibre" from *Literature of the Americas*. 2001. Honolulu: Curriculum Research & Development Group, University of Hawai'i. Reprinted by permission of the author.

Curtis, Caroline. "Nawai the Net Maker" from *Life in Old Hawai'i*. 1970.

Honolulu: The Kamehameha Schools Press. Reprinted by permission of The Kamehameha Schools Press.

ho'omanawanui, ku'ualoha meyer. "Ho'okupu" from *Huli Au 'Ōiwi 3, A Native Hawaiian Journal*. 2003. Honolulu: Kuleana 'Ōiwi Press. Reprinted by permission of the author.

Kalahele, Imaikalani. "Make Rope" from *Poetry and Art*. 2002. Honolulu: Kalamakū Press. Reprinted by permission of the author.

Kalama, Olga Kalei. "Ku'u Wā Li'i Li'i I Lā'ie." Prepared as a class exercise, given to Bill Teter.

Kanae, Lisa Linn. 1999. "Lei Maker" from *Look My Daughta and Other Poems and Prose: A Thesis Submitted to the Graduate Division of the University of Hawai'i in Partial Fulfillment of the Requirements for the Degree of Master of Arts in English*. May 2002. Honolulu. Reprinted by permission of the author.

Kaona, Lino. "MAKE Manu: MANU Make (*dead bird: death bird*)" from *Ho'omānoa: An Anthology of Contemporary Hawaiian Literature*. 1989. Honolulu: Ku Pa'a Incorporated.

Makua, Temujene Hanae. "Love Is All We Need" from *Write On, HEA!* 2001. Honolulu: Hawaii Education Association. Reprinted by permission of the author.

Tua, Jasmine. "They Called Him Mango Man" from *Write On, HEA!* 1998. Honolulu: Hawaii Education Association. Reprinted by permission of the author.

Aea, N. Keonaona. "Bearing the Light" from *Mālama: Hawaiian Land and Water*. 1985. Honolulu: Bamboo Ridge Press. Reprinted by permission of the author.

Akana, Keith Kalani. "Press Down" from *Bamboo Ridge #84: The 25th Anniversary Issue*. 2003. Honolulu: Bamboo Ridge Press. Reprinted by permission of the author.

Balaz, Joseph P. "Spear Fisher" from *After the Drought*. 1985. Honolulu: Topgallant Publishing Co., Ltd. Reprinted by permission of the author.

Beamer, Keola. "Old Man Pueo" from *Jack de Mello Presents Keola & Kapono Beamer: Hawaii Then and Now*. 2001. Honolulu: Music of Polynesia. Reprinted by permission of the author.

Edel, Marjorie. "Fishpond" from *The Place Your Body Is*. 1984. Honolulu: Petronium Press, Distributed by University of Hawai'i Press. Reprinted by permission of the author.

Hall, Dana Naone. "Ka Mo'olelo o ke Alanui: The Story of the Road" from *Ho'omānoa: An Anthology of Contemporary Hawaiian Literature*. 1989. Honolulu: Ku Pa'a Incorporated. Reprinted by permission of the author.

Kahanu, Hina. "Waimaka" from *Bamboo Ridge #77. 2000*. Honolulu: Bamboo Ridge Press. Reprinted by permission of the author.

Kahumoku, George, Jr. "A Shark Attacks" from *A Hawaiian Life*. 2001. Lahaina, HI: Kealia Press. Reprinted by permission of the author.

Kauihou, Danielle Ka'iulani. "Ka I'a" from *Kūnihi Ka Mauna 'Ōiwi 2, A Native Hawaiian Journal*. 2002. Honolulu: Kuleana 'Ōiwi Press. Reprinted by permission of the author.

Kinney, Jeanne Kawelolani. "Redrawing the Big Island" from *Bamboo Ridge #69*. 1996. Honolulu: Bamboo Ridge Press. Reprinted by permission of the author.

Malo, Makia. "Lo'i Kalo" from *Bamboo Ridge #73*. 1998. Honolulu: Bamboo Ridge Press. Reprinted by permission of the author.

Perkins, Leialoha Apo. "The Beach at Napali" from *The Firemakers and Other Short Stories of Hawai'i, the Sāmoas, and Tonga*. 1986. Honolulu: Kamalu'uluolele Publishers. Reprinted by permission of the author.

Pukui, Mary Kawena. "He Huaka'i Ka'apuni ma Hawai'i (Ramble Round Hawai'i)" from *The Echo of Our Song: Chants and Poems of the Hawaiians.* Mary Kawena Pukui and Alfons L. Korn, eds. & trans. 1973. Honolulu: The University Press of Hawaii. Reprinted by permission of the University of Hawai'i Press.

Emerson, N. B., ed. "He Mele He'e Nalu (A Surfing Song)" from *The Echo of Our Song: Chants and Poems of the Hawaiians.* Mary Kawena Pukui and Alfons L. Korn, eds. & trans. 1973. Honolulu: The University Press of Hawaii. Reprinted by permission of the University of Hawai'i Press.

Sinclair, Marjorie. "Lava Watch" from *Sister Stew: Fiction and Poetry by Women.* 1991. Honolulu: Bamboo Ridge Press. Reprinted by permission of the author.

Sylva, Rene. "Native Plants" from *Mālama: Hawaiian Land and Water.* 1985. Honolulu: Bamboo Ridge Press. Reprinted by permission of the author.

Trask, Haunani-Kay. "To Hear the Mornings" from *Night is a Sharkskin Drum.* 2002. Honolulu: University of Hawai'i Press. Reprinted by permission of the University of Hawai'i Press.

Trask, Haunani-Kay. "Returning to Waimānalo" from *Ho'omānoa: An Anthology of Contemporary Hawaiian Literature.* 1989. Honolulu: Ku Pa'a Incorporated. Reprinted by permission of the author.

Wake, Bryan Hiroshi. Excerpt from *Eddie Would Go.* 2005. Honolulu: Honolulu Theatre for Youth. Reprinted by permission of the author.

Aldosa, Mary Beth. " 'Au 'A 'Ia" from *Bamboo Ridge #84: The 25th Anniversary Issue.* 2003. Honolulu: Bamboo Ridge Press. Reprinted by permission of the author.

Armitage, Kimo. "Uncle's Drum" from *Bamboo Ridge #79.* 2001. Honolulu: Bamboo Ridge Press. Reprinted by permission of the author.

Brooks, Kahi. ". . .at heart" from *Huli Au 'Ōiwi 3, A Native Hawaiian Journal.* 2003. Honolulu: Kuleana 'Ōiwi Press. Reprinted by permission of the author.

Burgess, Puanani "Hawaiʻi Ponoʻī" from *Growing Up Local: An Anthology of Writing from Hawaiʻi*. 1998. Honolulu: Bamboo Ridge Press. Reprinted by permission of the author.

Burgess, Puanani. "Remarks: Regional Constructions of Cultural Identity Forum" from *Bamboo Ridge #73*. 1998. Honolulu: Bamboo Ridge Press. Reprinted by permission of the author.

Cataluna, Lee. Excerpt from *Super Secret Squad*. 2002. Honolulu: Kumu Kahua Theater. Reprinted by permission of the author.

Chock, Eric. "Poem for George Helm, Aloha Week 1980" from *Hoʻihoʻi Hou*. 1984. Honolulu: Bamboo Ridge Press. Reprinted by permission of the author.

Holt, John Dominis. "Pono," excerpt from *Hanai, A Poem for Queen Liliuokalani*. 1986. Honolulu: Topgallant Publishing Co., Ltd. Reprinted by permission of the author's family.

Kalahele, Imaikalani. "The Source" from *Poetry and Art*. 2002. Honolulu: Kalamakū Press. Reprinted by permission of the author.

Kaopio, Matthew. "The Boy Slept Under the Bridge" from *Written in the Sky*. 2005. Honolulu: Mutual Publishing. Reprinted by permission of Mutual Publishing.

Kikiloi, Kekuewa. "Desecration: The Bone of My Contention" from *Huli Au ʻŌiwi 3, A Native Hawaiian Journal*. 2003. Honolulu: Kuleana ʻŌiwi Press. Reprinted by permission of the author.

Kimura, Larry Kauanoe Lindsey. "Ua Ao Hawaiʻi" from *Huli Au ʻŌiwi 3, A Native Hawaiian Journal*. 2003. Honolulu: Kuleana ʻŌiwi Press. Reprinted by permission of the author.

Meyer, Manu Aluli. Intention and its role in knowing something, excerpt from "The Role of History, Intention, and Function: More Thoughts on Hawaiian Epistemology, " from *Huli Au ʻŌiwi 3, A Native Hawaiian Journal*. 2003. Honolulu: Kuleana ʻŌiwi Press. Reprinted by permission of the author.

Pukui, Mary Kawena and Caroline Curtis. "Can You Keep a Secret?" from *Tales of The Menehune and Other Short Legends of the Hawaiian Islands.* 1960. Honolulu: The Kamehameha Schools Press. Reprinted by permission of Kamehameha Schools Press.

Takehiro, Sage U'ilani. "'Anakala Kalāhele's Love-Hate Lecture" from *Honua.* 2007. Honolulu: Kahuaomānoa Press and Kuleana 'Ōiwi Press. Reprinted by permission of the author.

Uchima, Ululani D. "I Geddum" from *Huli Au 'Ōiwi 3, A Native Hawaiian Journal.* 2003. Honolulu: Kuleana 'Ōiwi Press. Reprinted by permission of the author.

Osorio, Jamaica and Ittai Wong. "*Kaona.*" Composed for Youth Speaks Hawaii, performed at Brave New Voices, Washington, DC. 2008. Printed by permission of the authors.